The Girl whose mom used to be a mermaid

By

Jane Berg

janeberg.net

First edition published in Sweden, 2021

A C Creative Ecolution AB production

creativeecolution.com

ISBN:978-91-987034-2-9

To my wonderful children

Content

A Lovely Spring Day

Today is one of those beautiful, nearly magical, Spring days. Oh, how fun it would have been to race with mom today and chase each other around the orchard. Like we always used to do on days like this. Mom always wins. When she does, she usually tickles me so that our laughter and screams echoes between the trees and flies like happy birds up, up, up to the sky. All is different this Spring. Smilingly mum assures me that it will be back to normal soon. But dad's sad eyes and avoiding glaze tells me that it will not be. Of course, mum still manage to come up with funny ideas and make me run around in the garden, in the park or on the beach. Had it only been fatigue and mum's problem with running, I would not have minded. Not even the fact that she can barely walk right now, would be so saddening. But some days I can clearly see how much pain she is in. And that tears my heart up. There is nothing I can do to make that go away. Clearly it tears dad's heart up to. When it does, he usually disappears into the garage and build stuff. Yesterday he had finished a beautiful box in walnut tree, elegantly decorated.

"For your beautiful ideas, my love", he had said when he gave it to mum after dinner. With happy tears in her eyes, mum caressed the box and said what an extraordinary delicate box dad had made. Before he knew it, she would fill it with the most superb ideas ever, mum concluded with a wink.

Today mum sits in the garden in her favourite garden chair. She has a blanket over her knees and she is reading a book. The box is on the table. My legs are dangling from the swing and I enjoy feeling the breeze against my face. I run over to her from the swings that hang in the big tree.

"Bella, Stella my favourite star", mum chants and lifts her arms for a hug. We hug for a while. She kisses me on the cheek. I ask her how many beautiful ideas she has gathered today. With a smile she says three. Mum asks me to sit on her knee so that she can tell me a story. I love when she is telling stories. Today she tells me the story of the seagull who did not want to grow up. After she has finished the story we sit quietly for a while and listen to the birds singing and how the leaves try to follow. Then I ask her. I have been meaning to do it for a long time, but I have not had the nerve to do so. But today is the day when I ask my mum what is wrong with her. Why can't she run like she used to? Why is she always so tired? And why is she in pain? With her right hand she strokes the hair out of my face. She kisses my forehead and hugs me. But she does not say anything.

"Mum?" I try.

"One day, bella Stella, I will tell you the story. Today is not that day so let's enjoy the birds and the leaves and welcome Spring by running as fast as you can three times around the house. I will clock you", mum says enthusiastically. And I fall for it, again.

In the evening after dinner mum goes upstairs to rest. Me and Dad clean the table.

"Dad", I say.

"Yes, Stella darling, what is it dear?", dad wonders.

"I am old enough to know something is wrong with mum. Why don't you tell me?" I question.

"I know Stella darling. But sometimes you just have to be a bit patient. Let mom tell you when she is ready. Is that ok with you?" he asks with his calm, deep, slightly sad voice. I nod my head and go up to my room to play. Tomorrow is a school day. I am in third grade and barely have any homework's. I love learning new things. I do like my teacher, but I am not super fond of all my school friends. Especially not those three girls in my class. They are mean and stupid. Dad says I am not allowed to say things like that. So, I do not. But I think them! For my last birthday I got a beautiful turquois diary with butterflies on the front in a silky shiny fabric. Nearly every day I write something in it. I try to write at least something good for anything bad. Usually, it is something I have done with my parents or they have taught me. Today I will put down patience. Not sure that I have learned it yet, but it feels good to write it down none the less. Before closing the diary, I decide to start with something new. I will start scribbling down my good ideas just like mum does with the notes in her new idea box.

A Normal School Day

For being a school day nothing special happened. The three stupid ones were perhaps a bit meaner than normal, but they did not really do anything. Most of the time I was longing for mum and looking out the window. One time, when I was thinking about the tandem bike, we were riding on in the orchard last Spring, I laughed out loud. Obviously, the most obnoxious of the three ones seized the opportunity to ridicule me and call me names. Even though I did not let it bother me that much I could not help but thinking that I would need to come up with an action plan to stop this. Despite my young age, I knew enough about how bullying starts and how it easily can escalate if you did not manage to turn it around in time. During the breaks I still had my good friends to play with. Too bad they did not go in my class. Amanda wondered if I wanted to come and play at hers after school. Of course, I would have loved too, but I had to say no. During weekdays it was nearly impossible now adays to go to someone else's house after school. Dad worked too late to pick me up and mum would not manage to drive the car right now. Since Amanda lived on the other side of the village from me, neither mum nor dad would approve of me walking home alone. In a few years' time dad said I would be allowed to. Instead of asking Amanda to join me after school I said that if possible, I would love to come to hers at the weekend instead. I was hundred percent sure dad would give me a lift then. Today was one of those days when I did not like to walk home alone. Luckily enough my other friend Isac, lived halfway in the same direction as me. Normally that was enough for keeping the mean girls away, and whatever entourage they had with them as well. The fact that Isac already at the age of 8 was a tall and strong boy playing all sorts of sports, probably helped a bit as well. On top of that Isac had three older brothers that each of them was bigger, stronger and faster than the other. So normally the first half of the way home was safe. It was after Isac had turned off and I continued on my own, there could be real problems. This, I had not told my parents. Without any doubt they had enough worries already. A bike would have been handy. I knew they would never catch me if I was on a bike. Last year I made a choice to wish for a tandem bike instead of a normal bike. So therefore, I had no bike to school now. No way the tandem bike would be of any use trying to outrun the three stupid girls. The bike itself would just provide them with more ammunition. Then riding a tandem bike on your own was quite tricky and it took a while before you got up to speed. Some days it felt like their sole purpose in life was to find odd things about me that they could pester me about. So, I practised my running skills.

Mum and her fantastic smile were waiting for me at the gate. She stood there leaning on the fence as support. I wondered how long time she had been standing there. We hugged like we had not seen each other for a long time. Today, that was exactly how it felt. It had been a long day with very few new things to learn. As per normal I was curious to hear about mum's day. Mum just laughed at my eagerness.

"Well, I do actually have something to share. I did not only come up with 3 ideas but five, have you!", mum said cheerfully and cocky.

I got very excited and wanted to hear all about them on the spot. But since it was a weekday there were rules. Doing my homework and cocking dinner came first. Sharing ideas and stories was for after dinner.

Up in my room I unpacked my school bag. We had got one homework in maths and one in English. The math homework was an easy one, so I decided to do that directly. The English homework was not so easy. All the pupils had a week to write an essay about anyone in their family. The teacher would pick out the three best ones and read them out loud in the classroom. However, she would not reveal the names of the authors. Mainly because all the practise I had had, I was quite confident that my essay would be one of the three. It usually was. For any other pupil in the class this might have been something to look forward to, to feel proud of and good about. But for me, I knew that if I wrote about my family, the stupid ones would understand it was my essay directly and they would make fun of me and my family in front of the whole class for days. Perhaps even weeks. Since my family is so precious to me, I do not allow anyone to laugh at them. If anyone wants to laugh at me, that is a different story. That does not bother me at all. Therefore, I decided to make up a story about a girl with no siblings and then tell a story that would be about her make-believe mum – not my mum. That would be close enough to reality and I was sure the teacher would allow my artistic freedom. With a determined mind I grabbed the pen, looked out the window and slammed the notebook on the desk. Roughly ten minutes later the only sentence I had written was:

"Close by the sea, in a small village famous for its fabulous orchards, our heroine rests her tired feet laying in a hammock with a hat over her face. Happy, she hums a song." That was it. Now I obviously needed to come up with a story which would transform my character into a heroine. Hmmm, my mind was blank. Normally I had too many ideas. My thoughts wandered away as I followed the movements of the clouds. Some time passed but I still had no idea what to write about. Mum called me down for dinner.

Mum's Story

Downstairs I found out that dad was finally home. When dinner was over, and everything were washed and cleaned away, mum said it was a story night tonight. With a wide smile on his face, dad kissed mum and said that in that case he would be doing some drawing while she was telling the story. I was thrilled. After dinner, the three of us sat down in the winter garden. The sun was settling down, still not ready for going to sleep. Perhaps it was waiting for mum's story as well. Mum sat down in her chair and wrapped the special blanket grandmother (dad's mother) had made her last year, around her legs. Me and dad sat in the sofa with the floral fabric. Dad took the right seat with his drawing pad in his knee and I took the pink blanket and the left corner. I was so excited. The aroma from my favourite tea made the evening smell even more magical. With a smile mum cleared her throat:

"It was a normal day. Together with her sisters she was playing dodgeball with some of their friends. The sea urchins were relieved that they were being asked to be judges instead of balls. Their dad had got some complaints earlier, so he asked the neighbours to make a dozen of sea balls made of seaweed for his daughters´ sports activities. How she enjoyed playing this game! In fact, she loved playing most games. Her dad and mum tried to get her to work on her temper though... As much as she loved winning, as much she hated losing. She must admit, she was not very proud of herself when she was losing. Today she had picked her team and she was sure they were going to win. And after the game they were all going to get ready for the big party later in the evening. The party was to celebrate her parents renewing their vows. Basically, the whole kingdom would be there. For weeks they had been decorating the castle. Her two oldest sisters were already engaged and were to be married later in the year. Now everyone was expecting her to get engaged. The amount of effort her mum had put into her outfit, she assumed her parents already had someone on their minds. "

Mum paused for a while and took a sip of her tea. Then she smiled at me.

"The game was intense. The crowd was loud and excited. The swordfish in her team was the real hero. With him and the stingray she knew that she could win the national tournament. They probably even had a great shot at the championship in this part of the ocean. Dad had said he thought she was getting too old for this though. According to him she needed to focus on the future and go into proper training. Whatever that was. One of her older sisters was in her team and the other big sister was in the opponent team together with their little

14

sister, a cousin, an octopus (nearly cheating if you asked her) and a turtle (okay, that balanced it out a bit). The other team was good but not as good as her team. Her team was leading the second round with only the third to go. It surely looked like an easy win. Plenty of journalists were watching them from the stands. Obviously, it was not only the game that had attracted them. The royal party with the free food and free drinks, was more likely to be the real reason for their presence. The swordfish was having the game of his life. Azalea, her oldest sister just caught an exceedingly difficult ball from the other team. As in any good story, there was a sudden turnaround in chain of events. A very predictable game turned into everything but that when the swordfish broke his nose on an oddly screwed ball from the octopus returning Azalea's ball. While her friend, the swordfish, was crying his eyes out from pain a young man was standing in a circle of friends close by in the crowd and he was laughing. Even though it was making her angry she tried to ignore it. Unfortunately, the doctor's verdict was that the swordfish could not continue playing. Nearly at the same time she heard the young man calling the swordfish a coward and the blood rushed to her head and without any self-control she lashed out at the young man. And as that would not be enough, the sea urchins refused to give a penalty to the opponent team. According to the sea urchins it was unintentional, but she knew they were being wrong. So, she screamed out that if they did not wind their necks in, she would use them as balls next time. And the time after that. Azalea grabbed her right hand and pulled her back to the pitch. With her back turned away from the obnoxious young man she heard how he continued saying mean things, but she managed to switch her focus back to the game. The remaining part of the game was a real struggle and turned out to be too difficult for her team and ended in pure disappointment."

Dad shows mum the sketch he has just made. It is a swordfish with a broken nose and very frightened sea urchins hiding in a corner of a dodge ball pitch. Both me and mum laugh out loud. The sun has coloured the evening sky red and small clouds are slowly drifting over the sky waiting for the moon to appear. Me and mum both sip on our tea. Her eyes smile happily at me. She continues:

"Back in her chambers she walked straight into the shower being both angry and ashamed. In a properly agitated state, had she just run off the pitch and away from the audience back to her room. Not good manners. She had not thanked the opponents as you should. Neither had she thanked the crowd nor the referee. With tears burning behind her eyes, she had had to run fast. In the background she heard boisterous voices laughing at her and calling her names. One voice had been particularly clear, the voice of the very same young man that had been mocking them during the game. Now he was pitying whoever was going to have to live with her, unless you enjoyed how easy it was to wind her up, that was. No way she was going to give the nasty young man or her annoying sister or cousin the enjoyment of seeing her cry. So, she scurried away from there as fast as she could. In her heart she knew so well what a baby she could be and that she needed to learn how to handle her emotions better. All the people criticising her temper were actually quite right. There was a gentle nock on the door. She assumed it to be the chamber lady delivering her dress for the evening. But it was her mum bringing the dress and a nice drink. Her mum hung up the dress and then she came up to her and gave her a hug and slowly stroked her hair. Mum always managed to sooth her and make her feel calmer and better. The dress was fantastic, even though she did not want to admit it. Preferably she would have worn something more casual, so she could go out and play after dinner. Today she was not allowed to do that. It would be the first time she was going to take part of the dance and the party following the formal dinner. Tonight, she would be formally introduced to the grown-up social world. Needless to say, she did not look forward to it. Most likely she would not be allowed the same type of free life which she had led up till now. From now on her life would follow more strict rules. The eyes had dried, and she looked at her mum and thanked her. Her mum was astonishingly beautiful and today she did not only have an amazing dress, but also her best jewellery on. With those fantastically warm and understanding eyes, her mum made her get ready without feeling too pressured by the party. That was for real an amazing achievement.

Walking down the stairs she could feel all the guests staring at her. A few steps behind her was one of her two older sisters, Azalea, with whom she was very close. Azalea often reminded her of their mum, not only in looks, but more so with her manners and personality. She had to push away the instinct to wipe her sweaty palms on her dress. Every time she got nervous, she got sweaty palms. Azalea had told her to think about the best book or story she knew. Preferably a quite funny one. That way she would be slightly smiling and not looking directly at the guests, but just easily glide down the stairs to mum and dad. It was a great tip. Before she knew it, she was standing next to mum and dad. Her dad put his strong arm around her shoulders. Then her dad made a noise to attract attention since he clearly had something important he wanted to say. All eyes turned towards them. Unconsciously she moved away from her father to get out of the spotlight. She did not get very

18

far until she felt her father's strong arm on her left shoulder pulling her back. This time he pulled her even closer to him. With his strong, deep timbre, he welcomed all the guests and went on to express how humble and glad it made him and his fantastic wife, that so many of their bellowed family and friends had come to celebrate this precious occasion with them. His hand still kept a firm grip of her left shoulder. After several minutes with more words from her father she felt him squeezing her shoulder harder. Then she heard him talking about her and how she had grown up into an exceptionally special young lady. Today, he proclaimed, was an incredibly special day for both him and his wife; one of those days that clearly marks the beginning of something new and the ending of what has been. The Royal Family had an unbelievably happy announcement. Being the third princess in line to be engaged and to start her formal training, she the princess, would be moving away to the sea very far, far away, to study under the great master himself. The words felt like a dark fog sweeping into the palace. Perhaps this was all a dream? Not sure she understood what was going on, she turned her face to her mum to see if the words of her father would make more sense. All she could interpret from her mums' look was a strange combination of pride, shame and sorrow. It was like a freezing cold current just swept in over the big room in the palace. With pure horror she realised that nearly all the guests in the room were staring at her. A feeling of despair and panic started spreading through her veins out to the tip of her tail. While her heart was shivering from the cold sensation and her vision was blurred, she could see the crowd parting when her father declaring the engagement of his third daughter. Him, the king and his wife, the queen, were so very happy to announce the engagement between the third princess of the Middle Sea and lord Gabriel from far, far away. In the middle of the parting crowd approaching her with steady steps and a head worn high, was this young man. She recognised him, and it was not a pleasant recognition. It was the nasty young man from the game. When he reached out to grab her hand her whole being revolted. From the bottom of her tail, up through her body, via the heart for extra fuel, it finally reached her throat. A roar of despair and anger flooded the room. With force she broke free from her father's hand on her shoulder and she aggressively pulled her hand away from the young man. Then she fled and swam as fast as her fin had ever managed to swim. Through the angry pulse in her ear, she heard both her father and mother calling for her to come back. Probably there were even more people shouting and possibly it was Azalea she heard shouting in the background. But she did not care. Not at all. After swimming at a furious pace for a while, she was not that angry any longer but more sad. The tears did not stop her though. Like someone chased by a crazy white shark she swam further and further away from the royal palace. Millions of thoughts were running berserk in her head. Thousands of questions were asked. The biggest and most painful of them all was how the people she loved most in the world had utterly betrayed her. How could they? What sort of family were they that had tricked her so totally and without any shame??? She felt stupid, angry and broken hearted. The fin was moving slower for a while. All the emotions were not agreeing with her stomach. She made a short pause to throw up. Then she continued swimming fast without any direction but with tears running down her cheeks that would not just stop. Even mum and Azalea were in on it all. They all knew and lied and just wanted to get rid of her. Well, she did not ever want to come back. Never before, had she felt so abandoned and lonely.

After hours of swimming and crying she was absolutely exhausted and wanted to sleep. However, she could not stop swimming. There was no option, she just had to go on and get as far away from the palace as possible. In a haze of tiredness, she had noticed that it had gotten very dark, then for a while getting bright and then dark again. Despite the darkness she continued swimming until the morning came. Now it was afternoon again. She could tell from how the sun rays were reaching down into the sea and how they were lightning up the bottom below her and the wall on the cliff next to her. Most likely she had fallen asleep several times while still swimming. Soon there was no energy left. Her father had surely sent out many troops to look for her. She would never let them catch her. That motivation conquered her fatigue. In her half slumber she had accidently swam straight into a group of cranky tiger sharks. That had woken her up for a while and now her tail was a bit sore as well as the knuckles on her left hand. Despite feeling utterly sad and empty in her heart she could not help but to smile when thinking what great punches she had thrown at three of the tiger sharks that tried to scare her. Even though she could have used the magical token she had not needed to. Using the magical token could call for some unnecessary attention which would help her father's guards to find her. Now she found herself on more shallow water. It looked like a safe and soft enough place to sleep in. There were even some soft corals and some nice seaweed to make a perfect bed. Perhaps it was too open. A cave would have been better and given her more cover. Night would soon come again and in the darkness, she would not be able to find something better. This naturally flat plateau was covered with some sort of seaweed in a nearly woven pattern. It reminded of her quilt back home. The lack of sleep forced her to make a stop now anyway. This place just had to do. There was no room for fear in her tired brain. After she laid down and put her tail in the right position, she fell heavily asleep in less than five minutes."

"Thirsty", mum says. Dad goes into the kitchen and comes out with three glasses and some lemonade. Mum asks if I am tired. I shake my head. I just want her to continue the story, so I do not waste time speaking. She smiles at me and drinks some lemonade and sits there quietly staring at the stars for a little while. My parents look at each other lovingly and then mum resumes telling the story:

"Sometimes when you wake up having gone to bed crying, you wake up with a light, sort of cleansed feeling. That was not how she woke up this time. Instead, she woke up with a feeling that she could not breath. After a few seconds it was clear that some outer force was squeezing around her neck and made it very hard for her to breath. It was still dark, and her eyes needed to adjust to the lack of light. The horror was intense when she realised that there was an arm squeezing around her waist while another arm was squeezing around her neck. The arms were firmly pulling her closer to whoever was the owner of the arms. As she was staring into a set of large eyes fixated on her and a scary open mouth with a lot of white teeth, she could feel how more arms were grabbing and squeezing around her whole upper body. She could not move a muscle anymore. She could not even reach for her magical token anymore. There were so many arms, but she could not count them in the darkness. Instinctively she knew that this was not like the octopuses she used to play with when she was smaller. This beast was something else. Its head was enormous. She could not think. Her head was blank with panic and her frightened heart made her body like jelly. Obviously, she could not scream because the giant tentacles with its sucker rings were pressing on her throat. Neither could she chant to activate the magical token. She tried to talk to herself to calm down. Panic would not help. Suddenly she realised that this must be a giant squid. This was bad. Perhaps a tiny bit of panic would not hurt....

"Soo dear friend. Don't worry your pretty face. I will not eat you – yet", declared a disgustingly false-sounding slimy voice followed by a very nasty chuckle.

"I couldn't believe what I heard down in my little home. There was a mermaid resting up at shallow waters. Me and my gigantic eyes just had to see it for myself. And not just any mermaid I gather. You will be my most beautiful creature in my collection. Just relax. It will be sooo much easier for both of us. I really do not want to hurt you beautiful", the giant squid uttered panting and started swimming away with her in his solid grip. For the first time in her life, she gave up. There was nothing she could do. Lack of food made her feel like an empty doll. She was so afraid she could not even cry. Slowly they swam deeper and deeper down into the immense and dark sea. Petrified she wondered what the giant squid meant when he said he had a collection. Countless horror stories were told about vicious and wild sea creatures that captured various living beings from their near and dear ones. It was difficult to say how much truth there were to these stories, but surely there was a grain of truth in a few of them. As horrifying as it sounded, it could surely not be that he was capturing sea creatures for his own pleasure? That would be even worse than the horror stories Azalea used to tell her. If only Azalea was here with her! Then this would never have happened. Azalea would have found a safer place to sleep and she had been much more watchful and not let herself get caught like this. Down at this depth she had no vision. It was total darkness. The fear was so overwhelming that it all felt hopeless. The suction cups and the tentacles were pressing so hard around her body so that the mermaid could hear the octopus' hearts. At least two of them. Defenceless as she was, she started to come to terms with her cruel faith. Perhaps she cried, perhaps she did not. The giant squid was humming unpleasantly content while the darkness surrounded them as they submerged even deeper into the bottomless sea. Soon there, soon there, the squid was wheezing in her ear. In the distance you could hear low earie noises. Something told her she would have plenty of time to gloom, mourn and to long for her family and desperate wishing her back a week ago. The thought that her life was over, totally paralysed her and prevented her from being able to scream and fight back. The horrible insight of her utter loneliness squeezed her heart.

All of a sudden, the giant squid made a strange noise, and she could feel a strong jerk from the tentacles as the sea monster was thrown aside and a forceful wave hit her face. She nearly choked and got even more panicked. Then she was free and felt how she was caressed by an enormous fin. Now she was being pushed up from the deep see towards the surface. It was still so dark that she could not see anything. But she sensed a large shadow next to her. Finally, she could breathe. She was not afraid anymore. After a while it got lighter and the speed slower. A deep and calm voice hummed that she did not need to be afraid any longer. She would be taken to safety.

The saviour was a kind-hearted sperm whale that took her to a nice and calm bay. There he asked her many questions. Most of them she answered reluctantly and not entirely truthfully. In the end she asked if he could help her across the ocean to the western parts where she had family. The sperm whale promised to help her but he kindly concluded that he was travelling in a different direction. After a while he called for a group of dolphins, he usually collaborated with on his rescue missions. If she had not been so exhausted and famished, she would have asked questions about the rescue missions, but the dolphins arrived, and she forgot it. They were a happy and cheerful bunch. She got fed and got a chance to rest properly in their safety. The sperm whale said goodbye after the mermaid had got a nice long sleep. He needed to return to the deep sea to investigate what other creatures there were needed to be saved from the giant squid and his monstrous prison. The mermaid did not know how she would ever be able to thank him. He smiled kindly and answered that her being safe was reward enough. The dolphins swam with her further out to the open sea and told her that one of their good friends was waiting for them out there. Through the ocean express they had sent a request for a good travel companion for her, and they got a reply from one of the best ones. During the swim, the dolphins sang and rhymed, and she even learned one or two of their songs. The dolphins had a fantastic way of making her forget to be sad. The friend was going to take her across the ocean to where she wanted to go. Appearing in front of her was a huge blue whale. She had never seen one and was fascinated by its size and was amazed how silently the enormous whale had appeared from the deep sea. The dolphins made her promise to never forget them and to be careful. Then the blue whale helped her to cross the big ocean. It was a several days long journey. They did not speak a lot. The silence was soothing and beautiful. The blue whale told her that it was not the first time she had been the travel agent for a mermaid who wanted to cross the open sea and travel to the western parts. Perhaps it was a relative of hers? The mermaid nodded and felt bad about lying to her new friend. But she had come this far and could not risk being sent back to a life she did not want.

One day they reached a great bay. She, the big blue whale could not swim closer to the shore. It was not safe for her. So, the blue whale instructed her where to swim and how to avoid getting to neo close to the dangerous cliffs. Finally, she told the mermaid where to find the caves where she probably would find her family. The mermaid cried a bit and hugged the blue whale and wished her a safe journey down south. Cautiously the mermaid swam closer to the shore and found a good place to rest her fin and eat something. Later she would go and find herself a good cave. After having eaten she got so tired that she needed to lie down for a little rest. She fell asleep. Once again, she woke up in a bad way. First, there was a horrible noise shaking the whole sea. Then it felt like someone had placed a huge stone on her chest. After some time, she realised that there were a multitude of other creatures being squashed against her. There were sand and stones. She could hear them all screaming in many different languages. They were all panicking screaming out their angst and pain. The loud noise came from further up, above, closer to the surface. The surface that she had been taught to be very, very cautious of...

Caught in a net

The cold, unpleasant wind brought her back to consciousness. Dizzy, she found a pair of very blue startled eyes, staring into her own green groggy eyes. To say the least, she was confused. Fully awakened, she noticed that behind the fantastically blue eyes that belonged to a young man there was another young man that nearly looked the same. He was also staring dumbfounded at her. With huge difficulty she turned her head to the left to get a better understanding of where she had ended up. Slowly but surely, she realised that this was one of her nightmares. From what she saw this must be one of those ferocious fishing boats. Further in the back of the boat she saw an older man with a beard grabbing hold of fish and other sea animals and throwing them into some sort of tray. With a paralyzing fear, she noticed yet another older man without a beard that was in the front but on the opposite side. Since he was holding on to a wheel and was standing somewhat higher up, she understood that he must be the one in charge. Both the older men wore some sort of greenish clothes while the younger men had bright yellow clothing. The old man without the beard handling the fishing boat shouted something to the younger men. They shouted something back. She could not hear what they were shouting due to all the cries for help and screams of pain from

30

the fish gasping for air all around her. There was a very nauseating smell and she understood that it must be from the fish slowly dying around her. Never before had she noticed fish smelling like this. She was hurt. Both tail and the head were aching so much she was afraid she would pass out again. With a sense of despair, she realised, that with her injury there was no chance for her to break free and manage to flip back into the ocean. The boat was rocking back and forth, from side to side. The young man with the intense blue eyes was trying to sooth her and probably saying that all would be good. For some reason she could not really understand what the humans were saying. Then she tried to understand what the older man without beard was yelling:

"Throw her back immediately! Nothing good will come out of this! You have to listen to me son!"

The young man stroked back the hair that had blown into her face while he carefully tried to free her from the net she was still tangled up in. The wind was strong and loud but that was not the reason why she did not understand what the young man yelled in response...

"Dad, we cannot throw her back in to the sea, she is hurt and we need to take care of her!"

The sun had managed to find a hole in the clouds and shone on his blond hair making it look like gold. She smiled a bit and thought that he had a very lovely face and kind eyes. With his warm and soft voice, the man asked something she still did not understand while he was carefully untangling her tail from the net. Just as she was about to answer him that she did not comprehend, an unbelievable pain hit her like a giant wave and she passed out.

The four men were totally bewildered and had no clue what to do with this magnificent creature who by all accounts was a mermaid. They did the only thing they could do, they called for someone wise who would know what to do. They called for the wife of the captain which also happened to be the mother to the two young men. "

"Now Bella Stella, even though the other stars are fully awake and brighten up the night, you have to go to bed. It is a school day tomorrow my favourite star", mum says with a tired smile. Of course, I objected. How could I do anything else? I was totally captivated by mum's story and wanted to hear more. Going to bed was not part of the plan. However, I could clearly see that mum was tired and from the looks from my dad, arguing would do me no good. So up to bed I went, and I dreamt of this giant under water castle where the royal family were having to most amazing party in all colours of the rainbow and a beautiful sperm whale were singing lovely melancholic songs.

One of those days

School was finally over, and I was walking home together with Isac. We walked in silence. Isac was really good with picking up signals. Today I was not in a chatty mood. The three obnoxious trolls had excelled in meanness. After calling me names the whole morning things escalated in the afternoon at gym class. The smallest of the girls with the nasty eyes had stolen my clothes when I was in the shower. After searching for them everywhere I could possibly think of, I found them drenched in the toilet. Someone had peed there as well. Full of rage I simply walked out from the dressing room in to the teachers' lounge. Standing in the open door to the teachers' room I loudly and clearly declared that I had had enough and that I had no clothes on thanks to three horrible trolls had tried to flush them down the toilet after having relieved their blathers. Isac and Amanda's teacher came up to me still holding her cup of coffee in her left hand.

"We cannot have you running around naked despite those trolls, can we now?" she questioned calmly with a kind smile. She asked me to come in and sit down in one of the chairs. Most of the other teachers that had been in there scattered away from me like nervous rabbits. The gym teacher came barging in and hollered:

"What do you think you are doing young lady? Running around on the School premises without any clothes on!"

"Well, she got a towel", corrected Isac and Amanda's teacher. "Perhaps you need to control some of the other pupils a bit better so certain students do not have to run around in school with nothing but a towel on.

By this time my own teacher had realised that it was me in the middle of the commotion. Obviously, she was wondering what was going on. I did not say much. She did not give up, she kept on going at me.

"Stella, how many times have I not told you not to provoke those girls? You cannot continue like this. I will have to call your mother!" I begged her not to. Nearly panicking I argued that she would be asleep, and mum should not be disturbed because she was not feeling too well. She repeated the threat. Rachel, Isac and Amanda's teacher, stepped in and handled the situation.

"Let's try to find some spare clothes for you Stella. And you, Rachel turned to the gym teacher, bag the wet dirty clothes please!"

In one of the teachers' toilet, I got dressed into the clothes that Rachel had picked from the lost and found basket. Rachel gave me a hug and told me that sometimes grownups were useless at handling mean girls. I should not judge my teacher and the gym teacher too harshly, she pleaded. I did not actually. I only despised the three mean trolls in the shape of girls. Life had already taught me that even adults could be real cowards and not worth vesting your energy on. The rest of the afternoon had dragged on worse than ever. Here we were, me and Isac, walking in silence. I had my backpack on my back and a plastic bag with the scruffy clothes in, in my left hand, trying to be as discreet about it as I could. From time-to-time Isac glanced at it without asking anything. I appreciated him greatly for it. He was truly a very good friend! Today, we walked slower and more relaxed than for a long time. As a consequence for their behaviour, the three mean girls got a detention today and would be yet another hour behind us. When we reached the spot where Isac turned off for heading home, he gave me a hug. I could feel the tears burning behind my eyes. We stood there hugging for quite some time and I mumbled thanks for him being such a great friend. Even though I did not have to today, I ran the last bit home.

Luckily enough, mum was not waiting at the gate. So, I managed to sneak into the house and hide the dirty wet clothes in the washing machine without anyone noticing. Walking out from the washing room I heard voices. They came from the winter garden. To my surprise it was mum and dad. Dad was home early. As soon as I stepped into the room they stopped talking. The atmosphere was odd. My father's eyes were sadder than ever. Mum stared out into the orchard. After a while she turned her head and asked how my day had been. Her eyes had a peculiar look - full of love, happiness and sorrow. Good, I lied. What else could I do?

"Are you hungry, bella Stella?" she asked me. I just shook my head in answer.

"Good", she declared. Then my idea is that you and Dad go and get us some nice drinks and then I can continue with the story. And when we get hungry, we just take some lasagna from the freezer. Does that sound like a plan?"

I exclaimed: "fantastic" and was shortly on my way to the kitchen. In the passage to the kitchen, I turned around and saw how Dad gave mum a long gentle kiss.

What to do with an injured mermaid?

"With resolute steps the beautiful woman came walking on the jetty. The thick, grey and curly hair was attempting to free itself from the kerchief covering it. When she came closer to the fishing boat and the three men standing there, she stopped and looked at the men with a piercing gaze. The young man with the blonde hair and amazing blue eyes were kneeling and holding the right hand of the passed-out mermaid. You could clearly see the resemblance between the woman with the kerchief and the young man. They had the same high cheek bones, the same shape of their lips and eyes with an identical intense blue colour. Without a word she kneeled down next to her son and took the girl's left hand in hers. Carefully she checked for pulse, examined her head while moving the dark brown hair away from the girl's face. Without uttering a single word, she finished the examination of the unconscious girl that carefully had been laid on the jetty.

"So you managed to catch and injure a mermaid", the woman concluded drily. The men mumbled.

"From the look of her clothes she is royal. Any plans what to do now?" she queried with a crisp voice. The men mumbled some more. The older man without the beard suggested they should throw her back into the sea. Then the young man with the blue eyes burst out and strongly argued that they needed to take care of her. She was injured, for god's sake!

"Of course, we shall my son", the woman said and put a gentle hand on the young man's shoulder.

"And you, dear husband, are an idiot! If you throw her back into the sea she will most likely die. We need to make sure she gets better first. So now soak one of the blankets into water, wrap the blanket around her injured tail and carry her out to the truck. I will take her home and make sure we get some expertise help here. We don't need to challenge the creatures of the sea. We do not want them furious with rage and seeking for revenge. Do we now dear husband?"

She did not wait for an answer but turned around and walked back to the truck waiting for the young man with the blue eyes, carrying the mermaid with a wet blanket wrapped around her tail. In the truck the woman made sure the young man covered her upper body properly with a warm blanket and tried to hold her head as steady as possible.

Once in the house, the woman with the kerchief and her son hastily constructed a bed for the injured mermaid. In the living room on the floor, they put a bench and laid a double folded mattress on top of it and at the end they placed a zinc basin filled with water in which they rested the mermaid's tail. Then they cleaned and took care of the head wound.

"Christophe, my son. I do know how to take care of head injuries, but I do not know how to take care of an injured mermaid's tale. In fact, I do know very little about mermaids. So, I will go and get some help from a person I suspect knows a bit more", the woman said with a secretive smile. The door opened and the old man without the beard and the other young man came into the hallway.

"Good you're home. I need to use the car", the woman said.

"Where are you going?" asked to older man.

"Vernon honey, I need to get some help with this mess. We will be back as soon as possible".

"Where are you going Charlotte?" wondered the man still in a bit of a shock. The woman called Charlotte told him not to worry but to make sure that someone was watching the mermaid in the living room to make sure that she did not stop breathing. Then she put her clothes on and grabbed the keys to the car. Instead of getting a doctor she had decided to go and get help from someone she knew very well, an old widow living on the very outskirts of the village. People usually referred to her as the willow tree witch.

A storm was raving in the sky.

"The sea seems to be upset", Charlotte, the woman with the kerchief was telling herself.

She was driving fast but safe. Although black clouds were filling the sky there was still no rain. Charlotte had driven these roads so many times she could nearly do it with her eyes blind folded. When she turned off the road by the old wooden house situated on the seaside, just by the huge cliff and where the road made a vast turn to the left around the cliff, Charlotte could see the old widow standing in one of the windows. It looked as if she was expecting her. Charlotte stepped out of the car and she had barely walked pass the fantastic willow trees on each side of the gravel walkway, when the widow opened the door for her. Her kind eyes welcomed Charlotte inside. The widow wore a beautiful turquoise dress that was so long it covered her feet. Over that she had an amazing, knitted cardigan. Her long hair was nowadays nearly white. Charlotte knew that it had been shiny black when she was younger. They hugged each other like they had not met for a long time even though it was just a week since last time.

"Sorry to disturb you but I have an urgent matter", Charlotte stated with her clear voice.

It was like the old widow had suspected that since she did not offer to take Charlotte's coat. She just nodded and started to put on her long grey raincoat.

"I am listening", she said while putting on her wellies with some difficulty.

Charlotte quickly told the old widow that it did not look better than her men had managed to catch and injure a mermaid today while they were out fishing. Of all the people she knew, she Lorelei, was the only person she could think of that would know anything about mermaids and how to treat them. The widow, Lorelei, gave Charlotte a long look and slowly nodded. Without a word she grabbed her handbag and keys and followed Charlotte out to the car.

The sky was now fully black, and it had started raining heavily. The wind was roaring over the skies and the cliffs. The sea appeared to try its best intimidating the small village in the bay. Even in this weather Charlotte drove fast but steady on the road going back to the house. The wind nearly swept the two women away as they were coming out of the car. With huge effort Charlotte managed to open the door to the house. It was nearly like the wind was trying to stop them going inside the house. When the two women finally entered the hallway, Vernon came up and took the coat from Lorelai. They nodded at each other before hugging each other quickly. No words were spoken. Lorelei walked slowly into the living room and in a trancelike manner carefully moved towards the injured mermaid with the tail in the zinc basin. She froze for a few seconds, stared at the girl in front of her and then surprisingly smooth took a seat next to the mermaid on the floor.

"Oh my, oh my, oh my", she whispered. Tears started falling down her cheeks. Then she sat quietly for a while and then with some difficulty got up on her feet again.

"Yes, she is a mermaid alright. You have done a great job", she concluded while drying her tears. "I will examine the tail, but I do guess it will heal itself. The head injury I am more worried about. I hope it is just a concussion. Perhaps you can hide her body and call for the doctor to look at her head? She is breathing fine so there seems to be no urgent need. You can leave it for a day to see if she wakes up. I would recommend you to keep absolutely quiet about having a real and living mermaid in your house. Otherwise, you might get all sorts of people here wanting to have their wishes fulfilled by the mermaid. Also, you should be wary about the sea. You do not know whose daughter she is and what they might do if they think you hurt her while fishing. I would really like to sit here alone with her for a while if that is fine with you".

Vernon, Charlotte and the boys were all in the living room. First, they looked bewildered at each other and then in unison they all nodded and made themselves scares.

Lorelai stayed with the mermaid for quite some time. Every now and then they could hear her chanting. Sometimes it turned into something sounding more like prayers or like she was reading poems to the mermaid. Then very clearly Lorelai started singing. The whole family stopped whatever they were doing at that moment, mesmerised by the most beautiful song they had ever heard. The voice sounded like the voice of a young woman and not an elderly widow. When the song stopped, they could hear movements, so they all walked into the living room where Lorelai now stood next to the mermaid with a peculiar look on her face. In some strange way she also looked at least 20 years younger.

"I will come here every day at 19.00 and perform my healing", Lorelai informed them.

They all nodded.

"So, who is driving me home?" she wondered.

"I will!", exclaimed Christophe a bit too fast and too loud.

He quickly helped Lorelai with her coat and grabbed the car keys that were on the green dresser in the hallway. It seemed that he could not get Lorelei out to the car fast enough. None of them said anything. The weather had calmed down a bit. It was not that windy any longer and the rain had stopped. Christophe broke off the silence and Lorelei's thoughts:

"I really hope you do not mind me saying this auntie", he started cautiously. "It was absolutely magical that song you sang back in the house". He took a short pause glancing at Lorelei that was still staring out into the night and towards the sea.

"Lorelei, I want to truly thank you. You did not have to come. But something tells me that you know something about that mermaid".

There was no answer from Lorelei. After a while Christopher wondered if she had not heard him. Naturally, he started repeating what he said but was shortly stopped by Lorelei.

"I heard you the first time Christophe. You are a very kind and perceptive man. You are right. I know more about that girl, a lot more. But even though I know your heart screams for knowing all about her I will not tell you what I know. What I will do is to help and heal her so you can hand her back to the Sea in which she belongs to", Lorelei answered with a definite but kind voice.

Christophe understood better than to push it. Nobody said anything more until they came back to Lorelei's house. Cordially they bade each other farewell and Christophe stayed until he had seen the old and still beautiful widow enter her house and securely closed the door.

Upon Christophe's return home, the whole family gathered in the living room with some tea and biscuits. First, they sat in silence and looked at each other then they looked at the mermaid.

"So, what did Lorelei say?", Charlotte asked her son.

Christophe looked down at the floor, then on the mermaid and lastly turning to his mother and said:

"She knows who she is but refuse to say anything. All she told me is that she will come here every night at 19:00 to heal her, as she put it.

"Good she checked with us first", Vernon, the dad, muttered.

"Stop complaining Vernon! You caused this. If you had been more watchful and handled the situation before it came to this, we would not have to involve Lorelei. We should all be very grateful she is helping us out here", Charlotte proclaimed with a sharp voice.

Vernon did not reply but looked like he did not agree with his wife.

"All of this; it's just surreal!", William, the youngest brother concluded.

Vernon nodded in agreement.

"Don't you all see how amazing this is! We are so lucky! How many people have ever encountered a living mermaid? Come on, you must agree with me!", exclaimed Christophe while he was waiving his hands seeking support from the others in his family. Charlotte put a hand on her son's shoulder and squeezed it lightly.

"Why are you all so scared? I do not understand!", Christophe wondered.

He got hushed by his dad that was nodding at the still unconscious mermaid.

Charlotte took her oldest son's hand and looked him deep into his marvellous blue eyes. With a calm voice she then told Christophe that yes, she agreed, it was fantastic. But as he must understand it was also quite terrifying. The fact that they now had a living mermaid in their living room was proof that the myth about mermaids was true. How could it not be? And from all the fairy tales and myths, she and their father, had been told since they were small children, nothing good could ever come out of having injured a mermaid while fishing. As Lorelei had said, who knew whose daughter it was they had in their living room, the sooner the mermaid went back to the sea the better for all of them. Christophe calmed down. He finished his tea and attended to the mermaid checking her breathing, the position of the neck and that the tail was properly placed in the basin. Then he said he needed to get some sleep and walked up to his bedroom. William also concluded it was time for sleep and excused himself. Vernon and

Charlotte sat for a long time in the living room holding hands and both of them thinking about the situation they now had ended up in. It brought back some long-time hidden memories to both of them. In the end it was Vernon who broke the silence:

"Soo shall we draw sticks on who sleeps on the sofa and minds the mermaid"? he said with a smile.

"Well, I don't want Lorelei to turn up here in the middle of the night screaming at us. I'll take the first shift, dear husband", Charlotte responded with a dry smile.

They kissed and Vernon went upstairs to go to bed.

Charlotte did not get more than 45 minutes of coherent sleep. The mermaid was making too much noise. Up until the others had gone to bed, she had been absolutely quiet. Charlotte reckoned she had been sleeping for around 30 minutes the first time she woke up by the strange noises she heard. It took some time before her sleepy brain realised that it had to be the mermaid making those sounds. Sometimes there was laughter and sometimes there was cries and even tears running down the mermaid's cheeks. Most of the time it was these odd sounds that must have been a foreign language from what Charlotte reckoned.

In the middle of the night Vernon came down to take his shift. Charlotte gave a quick briefing of how the night had been so far. Then she went upstairs to get some proper sleep. Or so she thought. It did not take longer than 40 minutes until Vernon woke her up with a wild look in his eyes.

"I think something is terribly wrong. She is making all these strange sounds and screams in her sleep", he nervously uttered.

"I think she might be dying".

Just woken up it took Charlotte some minutes before she understood what Vernon was saying. Even though he did not mean to, Vernon was a bit too loud than he should have been. Consequently, Christophe woke up and went into his parents' bedroom wondering what the heck was going on. Charlotte told him the mermaid was freaking his dad out. With a drowsy voice she told them to let her sleep. It was totally normal behaviour when you had suffered a concussion to make strange noises. It was the brain trying to heal, she told them and turned around to go back to sleep.

So, Christophe went downstairs to see what was wrong with the mermaid. Already at the bottom of the stairs he could clearly understand why his dad had reacted. From the living room there was a strange noise. It sounded like a mixture of singing, crying and chanting in a very peculiar language. Carefully Christophe sat down next to the mermaid and checked that her head was in a good position and slowly touched her chin. Sitting there he took the mermaid's right hand and held it tenderly while he whispered that he promised that all would be good.

The days past by and every evening at 19:00 sharp Lorelei appeared at the front door. Every evening Lorelei sat holding the mermaid's hands in hers while singing the magical songs and whispering words no one in the house could understand. No one but the mermaid, that was. The magical atmosphere filling the house even had an impact on William, the youngest son. When Lorelei was done and ready to go home on the fifth evening, Vernon asked if they could return out fishing the day after. Lorelei looked at him and said, not yet if he did not want to disappear in the deep ocean together with his sons leaving Charlotte all alone and heartbroken. A couple of evenings later Charlotte asked Lorelei to stay and have some tea with her. Somewhat reluctant Lorelei stayed.

"We start to have a bit of a situation here, Charlotte began. I have a husband who starts getting very stressed that he cannot work and provide for his family. I have a son who cannot leave the living room after you have gone – he is totally obsessed with her. Then I have yet another son and also a brother-in-law that are both literally driving me crazy and are soon ready to expose all of this if they cannot fill their days with something useful. As you might understand, I need your help and advice what to do here."

For quite some time the two women sat in silence. The steam from the hot tea enhanced the already supernatural aura around Lorelei.

"I fully understand that this is a difficult situation. But you will simply have to trust me. As long as the sea is roaring you cannot go out fishing. The sooner she gets well and can be returned to the sea, the better. Then I promise you the sea will be calm and you can go on with your lives like nothing has happened. Both you and me know that this is not the most hectic fishing season. They should be able to hold out for yet another week."

"Well, that is partly my concern. I do not think Christophe can. I have never seen him like this. I am worried he will cause trouble and not be so willing to let her go. Could you please talk to him?"

Lorelei agreed to do so the following evening."

Mum stopped talking. It was very late. Dad said that we had to resume the story tomorrow. If mom had the energy of course. It was very dark. You could see the stars but barely hear the sea. I was so tired and happy that I did not even protest. Also, I saw that mum was really tired. Dad asked if I could go in on my own. I nodded with a smile and dad lifted mum up and carried her inside.

A mermaid's wake up

I slept but dreamt so many strange dreams that night. When I woke up, I felt as I was in a different world. That odd feeling you can have when you have dreamt an intense dream, like you nearly live in parallel worlds, stayed with me the whole day in school. After school was finished, I could not even remember how bad the three mean girls had been during the day. I just grabbed the school bag and walked home without the normal company from Isac. Not fully certain, but I think I ran the whole way home. Today it was Friday so that meant that mum could continue with the story for even longer than yesterday. In the house mum was resting on the couch. So, I went upstairs to my room and started writing in my diary. After an hour I heard a knock on the door. It was dad who had got home a bit earlier than usual. He asked about my day and wondered if I wanted to help him with dinner. I wanted that. We let mum rest until dinner was ready. I really enjoyed helping my parents in the kitchen. While I set the table, dad went and got mum. Smilingly mum said that we would continue with the story as soon as we had enjoyed this fantastic meal.

"But perhaps Stella thought the story too boring, mum teased. Intensively I shook my head. Tonight, we had some sweets and nice drinks prepared when we took a seat out in the winter garden with the heating on.

"On the eight day the mermaid woke up. It was not Lorelei's singing that woke her up. It was a kiss on the cheek from a young man trying to comfort her when she was crying in her sleep. Charlotte was expecting her husband, who had been out fishing with his brother and youngest son, home soon. Christophe had refused to leave the mermaid. Even through the sounds from the radio that was on in the kitchen and all the many noises from the busy kitchen - sizzling frying pans, the sounds from casseroles and the fan - Charlotte could indeed hear the commotion out in the living room. Obviously, she had to go and see what was going on. In the living room, on the floor, there was a desperate mermaid and a Christophe with burning hot cheeks looking absolutely terrified. The mermaid was waving her arms and screaming and trying to move away as far as possible from Christophe but her inexperience with moving on land and her long tail made her just flounder like a fish panicking on the floor. Everything was chaos. The zinc basin was overturned and had been tossed to the other side of the room with the help of a perfect smash from the mermaid's tail. There was water everywhere. Charlotte tried to calm the mermaid down and spoke very slowly and softly. This was a futile attempt and had no effect at all, so she turned around and asked her son Christophe with a piercing look, what he had done to cause this turmoil. Not waiting for the answer, she ordered him to get a bucket and a mop to dry up the water. With a stupefied face Christophe did what he was told and dried up the water. In the meantime, Charlotte struggled to soothe the mermaid but each time she touched her shoulder the mermaid just screamed. In the end, there was no other option as Charlotte saw it, then to send Christophe to get Lorelai.

Time seemed to have stopped. The mermaid was still crawling around on the floor screaming. In the middle of it all, Vernon and William got home and when the mermaid saw them, she started screaming even more. The noise was unbearable. The men quickly ran away into the kitchen. Charlotte came soon after. There was not a chance on god's green earth that she could suffer all this screaming for much longer, she yelled. It sounded like someone was strangling ten seagulls in there, William uttered with a head nod towards the living room. Finally, their prayers were heard, Lorelei entered the house and walked straight into the living room and the terrified mermaid.

Christophe was the only one joining her, remaining standing still in the corner of the big living room. Quietly Lorelei started chanting. Despite her old age and aching body, she sat down on the floor and

54

slid easily towards the hysterical mermaid. The deep hypnotic voice grew stronger as the chanting echoed in the big room and from the ceiling the sound travelled across into the kitchen and throughout the rest of the house. Magically the mermaid stopped squealing. Calmly Lorelei put her left hand on the Mermaid's shoulder while she continued chanting. Then she pulled the mermaid closer and held her tight until she had the mermaid's head in her knee. Continuing to sing she signed to Christophe to take the zinc basin and signalled that he needed to refill it with water. By now Charlotte, Vernon and William were all standing in the doorway into the living room as well. Charlotte helped Christophe filling the bucket. Once the bucket was back into the living room filled with water Christophe carefully lifted the tail and put it back into the zinc basin. Then he backed off a bit. Mesmerised they all listened to the chanting now coming from both Lorelei and the Mermaid. It sounded like a beautiful duet in a strange, beautiful and mystical language.

After what must have been more than an hour the mermaid fell asleep and then Lorelei stopped chanting. With some difficulty Lorelei got up from the floor supported by Christophe. He helped with making sure that the mermaid was comfortable on the mattress on top of the bench and gently wrapped the blanket around her upper body. In the kitchen

Charlotte had prepared some tea and biscuits. They all sat down and waited for Lorelei to say something. And she let them wait. Then she let them wait a bit longer. With a longing glaze she stared out of the kitchen window towards the sea while she was sipping on her tea.

"As is understandable the girl was extremely scared and devastated", she informed them with a low voice.

They all nodded staring intensively at Lorelei.

"She had forgotten who she was and what had happened. Then she remembered and got even more scared. She thought you had kidnapped her or wanted to hurt her since you caught her in the fishing net. But I explained that you want her no harm and that you are good people", Lorelei explained as a matter of fact.

What she did not say, was that the real reason for the panic attack, was that while trying to grab the magic token around her neck to calm down and protect herself, she realised in horror that it was gone. It was a disaster. A magic token provides mermaids special powers that are needed for being able to communicate with all species in the sea and on land and for keeping safe, healing and do what humans refer to as "magic".

The others jut nodded again.

"What is her name?", Christophe wondered.

"Her name is Amberly", Lorelei nearly whispered.

"Amberly. What a beautiful name", Christophe answered with a dreamy voice.

Lorelei shook her head like she was shaking of some thoughts she wanted to get rid of. Then she looked Charlotte straight in the eyes and stated that there were some ground rules they had to go through. Clearly, they could still not tell anyone in the village about the mermaid. That would put her in great danger. Also, they should continue avoiding going out fishing since the sea would be very unpredictable and even dangerous until the mermaid had returned. Powerful sea people were looking for this particular mermaid and they would stop at nothing until they had her back safe and sound. They would have to feed her and keep her tail as still as possible in the zinc basin filled with salty water. Both her head injury as well as the tail seemed to have healed fine. If Charlotte could come home with her, Lorelei would prepare some food that she could bring back for feeding the mermaid. No food other than what she prepared was allowed to be given to the mermaid. The boys could take turns watching over her while Vernon and Charlotte were working.

"Vernon, you have to ensure that Ernest says nothing to no one and lie if you have to. I think it would be great if you can see if you also can look for a special kind of jewelry that the mermaid wore when you caught her. Perhaps it is still in the boat. I think it would mean a lot to her if you could find it", she said with a confident voice.

Then the session was over. Charlotte gave Lorelei a lift back home and later on returned with the food prepared for the mermaid.

After several days of nurturing, the mermaid started feeling better. Every now and then she cried and made strange noises. The two brothers spend quite some time with her and especially one of them used to sit next to her bed on the floor and read all different types of books. As per instructions from Lorelei they did not mention to anyone in the village about their special guest. Avoiding going out fishing was not difficult. The weather and the sea were still roaring, and daily storms continued along the coast and out at sea. Some brave fishermen went out for crab fishing though. The demand was still high and without the catch the restaurants could as well just close down. Mussels and oysters were still harvested. There had been some reports of injured pickers due to the storms but nothing serious. Charlotte was very busy in the family restaurant and William, Vernon and his brother Ernest and Ernest's wife all worked hard with keeping up serving the hungry guests and the bored fishermen in the village. Daily visits from Lorelei brought more food to Amberly and more chanting. Amberly had with the help of Christophe started to learn some words of English.
58

Christophe also helped Amberly with daily exercises of her tail. One day upon Lorelei's regular visits she found that Christophe and William had carried Amberly up to the bathtub. Lorelei quite concerned told them that this was good, but they should try to remember it was best with salt water for Amberly. Otherwise, it could dry out her skin in a bad way. When it became clear to both Charlotte and Lorelei that there was some strange tension between the two brothers, they went out for a long walk in the cold October weather. Through the windy village the two women walked holding each other's arms. The leaves swirled around them flying freely in the wind, some got tangled up in Lorelei's hair. Charlotte had her kerchief wrapped around her curly hair. When they returned it was noticeable how Lorelei was suffering from her rheumatism. As they came into the house, she walked with a lot of effort, nearly limping, Amberly was now back in the living room where Christophe held her right hand in his. Charlotte and Lorelei exchanged odd glances, but no one said a word.

The day after, Lorelei sits in the living room next to Amberly and Christophe and suddenly says:

"It is soon time for Amberly to return to the sea".

Just as she and Charlotte feared Christophe and Amberly reacted and nearly flung like they had been given a slap. There was a clear electric spark between Christophe and Amberly as they searched each other's eyes after hearing the words from Lorelei. The old ladies nodded and said in unison:

"As we thought".

Charlotte left the room and returned with some tea, as the situation required. Lorelei asked Christophe to move one of the chairs closer so she could have a proper sit. Once seated comfortably she asked the young man to come and sit next to her and Amberly. She would tell a story they both need to hear. Lorelei grabbed hold of Amberly's hand. Charlotte sat a bit further away in the sofa. Early morning turned in to late night as Lorelei told a long and partly sad story."

It is night now. The smell from the apple trees is fantastic. Mum strikes my hair. I have my head in her lap. I want to hear the rest of the story so badly, but the sleepiness has come over me and I am struggling to stay awake. After a while I can feel dad's strong arms around me, and I pretend to be fully asleep so he will carry me all the way to bed. Then I do not have to brush my teeth.

Changes and new beginnings

It was not the lovely Saturday morning as the stars had promised last night. It was actually the opposite. Outside the windows the apple trees were trying to shake off the rain and the apple flowers here flying around in the wind. We were all up early. Breakfast was quiet. Dad read the newspaper. After breakfast I helped out with the washing. Mum wondered if I wanted to go to Amanda's. I said I rather hear the rest of the story. Mum smiled and gave me a hug. If I did some of my homework she would continue in an hour or so. I did my homework. If you count staring at the notebook and waiting for words to magically appear so I could hand in my essay on Monday. Since the whole homework situation was far from productive, I decided to do some proper thinking and write down my good ideas instead. That was so much more satisfying! Finally, mum called me down and said it was story time. I ran down the stairs as fast as I could. Mum started with Lorelei telling a story.

"It all starts with a young mermaid being very upset with her older brother since he is constantly telling her that it is time for her to get married and live her own life. Her brother is soon to become the king.

He has two beautiful daughters and a very good wife. His wife has an open and kind face and heart, she will be the perfect queen. One day the parents to this particular mermaid and her brother are on their way back after a trip to the sea far, far away. A terrible undersea volcanic eruption kills their parents and the whole equipage. The young mermaid, which is soon to be introduced to society, loses both her parents, her governess and her nana the same day. The young mermaid first took comfort in minding her brother's daughters. The brother and his wife became king and queen and soon there was another child arriving to the world. The palace got even busier and there seemed to be no room for her. On a chaotic day with a strong current raving around the palace, her brother asks to speak to her in private. In a very grown-up fashion, the two of them alone in the tea parlour and then, pausing in between sips of the exquisite algae tea, he just said it: she would go to the country far, far away to marry one of the princes. It was for peace and stability and what their parents already had arranged on their last travel that ended in such a tragic way. With sorrow still taking up a lot of space in her heart she accepts and only asks for some more time. They needed to hire a new governess since she is not finished with her studies and she would like to help out more with the children. This they agree on and month's passes which turns into a couple of years. The young mermaid is very busy with her studies and playing with her nieces. Especially the youngest girl keeps her on her toes. The little girl was so full of life and with a golden heart. It was impossible not to love her. But she could be more than a handful some days. One day when the mermaid was out playing with her little niece, she decided that they needed to do something new. The little girl always wanted a lot of happenings and adventures despite her small age. The queen was pregnant again and the two older girls were now busy with their schooling. The mermaid decided to take the little niece out from the palace to the market. On the way to the market the girls saw a sea horse and the little niece got so excited that she just ran off to the other side of the road.

Lorelei sits quietly for some time before she continuous.

"While getting closer to the market the young mermaid had spotted the dolphin train coming towards the market in an enormous speed from the other side. If only it had stopped at the market. But it did not. Instead, they were coming their way and there was not just enough time for her to get to the little girl on the other side of the road before they had passed by. When the dolphin train was getting thunderously close little girl got scared and when she saw her on the other side of the road, she obviously wanted to get back to her auntie. The young mermaid screamed: stay there! Stay there! But the little girl did not hear her. The accident was unavoidable. The horror knew no borders and she literally thought her heart was going to stop. The ambulance came and took the little lifeless body to the hospital. Still today she can hear her brother screaming at her when he got to the hospital and was told by the doctors that the little princess would probably not survive the night. In total emotional chaos she ran out from the hospital and went to the old wise sea creature in the very end of town. She had heard that she could do magical things. It turned out that the stories where right. Oceania, which was her name, was a very peculiar combination of a green speckled moray eel for an upper body stuck to a lilac transparent jellyfish body with plenty of thin tentacles that were worryingly floating around and a few much thicker tentacles that appeared to be functioning as arms. For a second the mermaid considered to ask if she had been borne into this body but after staring into the sharp, quite scary eyes, she decided that it would be a bad idea. Rightly so, Oceania could do magical things, but it came with a price. In her case the price was to sacrifice her magical token for the girl's life. It was not a hard decision. Without the magical token handed down from her mother to herself she would be totally unsuitable for a marriage to the Kingdom far, far away. She would be unsuitable for any marriage. Well, she would be of no use to the royal family at all. She would be a disgrace. There was no other option now. She had to run away. So, she did. But before she left Oceania, she asked what to do. Oceania suggestion was a long journey and she told her the directions where to swim. It was a journey of many days. And she also told her she would have to meet yet another magical sea creature. Not entirely a good one, neither an evil one, but one who could help her to get a new life and some more useful tips for the future. She had to cross the great sea and find this mysterious creature in a large cave by a huge bay on the western side of the ocean.

Without given this a second thought she swam away. After a while there was some nice dolphins that offered to accompany Lorelei for a while. As they said, this was not waters she wanted to swim alone in. Especially a mermaid, a princess, without her magical token, one of them said raising an eyebrow at her. She pretended she did not understand what the dolphin was talking about. After several days they came to a group of Islands. The dolphins told here that this was their stop but that she was more than welcome to join them in staying here. She thanked them but said she had urgent business so she would only stay a night. The day after some of the dolphins joined her for a while as she continued her journey and told her that they would call for some old friends that normally travels these deep and dangerous waters to see if they could make the rest of her trip a bit safer. Gratefully she nodded and the dolphins began singing a summon song. Without having any proper sense of time, she waited while the singing was going on for, then they waited for a response. Through the immense, deep and dark ocean it finally came – the response was majestic and loud. She felt it in her whole body. Many times, had she heard stories of the great, majestic and enormously kind hearted and wise whale. Never had she seen one. The leader dolphin nodded to her with a kind smile. Slowly revealing itself coming closer she felt goose bumps all over her body. As the wonderful blue whale became fully visible, the leader dolphin swam towards the whale and together they surfaced. The mermaid was waiting down under the surface for them to return down back to her after they had caught some air at the surface. After a while they returned. She greeted the whale and got a fantastic greeting back. They spoke a bit. She explained where she was heading. The big blue whale said that she would be happy to take her on as a travel buddy and they would take the advantage of the current and stream as far as possible over the deep water. She could take a rest every now and then on her big back because this was rough waters and tough for a mermaid to swim in.

After a tearful goodbye to the dolphins the young mermaid and the blue whale were on their way. She had whispered to the leader dolphin to get a message through to the Mermaid King of the middle sea that his sister was sorry, but she was well and hoped that he one day could find it in his heart to forgive her. The leader dolphin promised he would personally make sure that the King got that message. The big blue whale was a great companion. Very rarely she spoke but her energy made the young mermaid calm and relaxed. Every now and then she had to stay under the surface on her own while the Whale went up to breath. Then they continued. Several times she saw sea creatures she had never seen before.   With a deep voice the whale told her the name of these creatures. The Vale told her many things she had never known before. The young mermaid was very grateful to her travel companion. Even though it was a long journey she made it quite pleasant and the mermaid nearly forgot how utterly sad she was.

One sunny day when they were swimming, they finally could see the cost. They got a bit closer to the shore where they said farewell. The Blue fantastic whale wished her all the best and hoped she would find what she was looking for. She also told the mermaid how to call for her or other blue whales if needed.

The mermaid swam fast. Without her magical token she felt very vulnerable and she could taste her heart in her mouth. She heard some orcas and sea lions and saw some sharks. Hopefully, they did not see her. After a close encounter with a large octopus, she finally saw what must be the cave she was looking for. Scared she swam up to it. When she got closer, she saw a massive port in dark wood with peculiarly beautiful and squiggly patterns. She chanted the hymn as Oceania had told her to. Nothing happened for a while, so she decided to chant some more. The port opened and appearing from the cave was a magnificent creature that told her to keep her voice down. She did not want to attract unnecessary attention to where she lived. Not everyone in the sea was her friend. The creature had the upper body of a mermaid and the lower body of an octopus and introduced herself as the great Membea. The mermaid greeted her and said her name was Lorelei. Membea exclaimed with an inquesitive smile:

"Oh, it's that Lorelei that has come to us for help."

They entered the cave. The heavy door closed behind them and Membea made sure it was locked properly. It was a beautifully decorated home in green, lilac and turquoise colours. Lorelei had never seen anything like this. After being seated on some cushions with the most magical and beautiful embroidery Lorelei got served soup and tea. Then she was asked to present her dilemma. Membea informed her calm and clear that she could offer different solutions. But she,

68

Lorelei, must understand it all came with a cost. She would have to give something up to gain something else. If the wish was to leave the life as a sea creature and enter the world above the surface, there were many things to consider for Lorelei. They discussed some of the major consequences if life on land was chosen. After some thinking Membea explained how she could give her an alternative to get a chance to try out life above the surface as a human being for 48 hours and before the sunset the second day she could go down to the ocean and call for Membea. Then they could revert it all and discuss other options. Lorelei felt this was the best alternative as she believed she could never go back to her old life. Without her family's magical token, she was basically not a royal mermaid any longer so why not try a totally different life above the surface.

The following morning the young mermaid woke up with a strange feeling in her body. It was a mixture of sadness and excitement. Membea put the medallion she needed to wear around her neck. It would not give her the old powers back, but it would give her the possibility to see into the heart of different individuals, always see the truth and partly also have the ability to see into the future. Finally, she would also gain some healing abilities through the medallion. However, she would not be able to use those on herself. The medallion needed to be worn at all times during the first 48 hours. Otherwise, her legs would turn back into a mermaid fin again. Lorelei followed the instructions on how to reach the shore and the land of the humans. As soon as she reached the surface her fin would turn into legs. Membea had already warned her that it would hurt but only for a short while. When Lorelei finally reached the surface, she understood that Membea was not exaggerating – it did hurt. But already fully up on land with her whole body it had stopped. The wind was strong and the temperature quite cold. Soon she realised that she did not have enough clothes. She was freezing. Membea had for two days described how the world of the humans' worked. But up here in reality, she felt very alone and scared. She did not really know anything and definitely not anyone. All she knew from the world of the humans were from books or various stories told to her through her life under the surface. Most of those stories where about the cruelty of man. Worriedly she looked up at the sky where some seagulls were showing off surfing in the wind. Mermaids considers seagulls quite nasty. If you happened to be close to the surface or even above, you could be sure that they would try to attack. No one had ever told her why. She has just followed the rules – keep away from humans and seagulls. Quietly she wondered what humans and seagulls thought of each other. Now she was here and trying to use these new pair of legs. It was difficult to keep the balance.

She already missed her tail. Awkwardly she moved forward. Sometimes more to the side than straight ahead. Slowly and with subdued mood she walked on the beach. It was empty. The chilly temperatures made Lorelei freeze into her bones. Every now and then she needed to stop and take a rest. Apparently not the best of ideas. When standing still in the wind she tried to get used to the toes. They were the strangest thing of all. She did not fully understand the purpose of having the foot split into different toes. Despite the cold, the odd feeling of not having a tail and that she was literally all alone in a foreign strange world, she could not help smiling at the toes as she was looking at them down there in the sand. Fascinated she realised that you could wiggle them. Spontaneously she burst out laughing and then she wiggled her toes so much that she lost her balance and fell over. Obviously, the mermaid did not know it yet. But this was what the land people called autumn. Soon it would get even colder. The mermaid looked around, but the rain and the wind made it difficult to see beyond the bay. She barely saw the cliffs, the sand on the beach and the sea behind her. Appearing across the other side of the bay there were what looked to be houses in shapes of different types of boxes. From this distance she could not see up to the cliff above the boxes where the orchards were spreading out and the leaves were painted in various colours.

After quite a walk across the bay she found herself so tired and cold that she needed to find shelter somewhere. Moving around above the surface was so different and much more tiring than moving around in the water. Also just breathing air made her lungs ache. The mermaid looked around trying to discover somewhere to rest. At this part of the bay there were some houses that seemed to be leading up to a small town. She picked a house that had the letters R E S T A U R A N T above it. As she entered her eyes widened with wonder as the place was very different than anything she had seen before. There was a young woman standing behind a disk – probably only a few years older than herself. Our young mermaid walked slowly with her head hanging low. The young woman in the restaurant had just noticed her and was now following the mermaid as she moved closer to the disk. The mermaid was quite nervous and stressed. She was concerned about if she would be able to speak and be able to make herself understood. With some efforts she opened her mouth and tried to say hi. Out came barely a beep. The young woman looked curious at her. The mermaid tried again. This time it was a proper sound, but the words tasted strange and she had no clue if what she just said was correct or not.

"Clay?" the young woman wondered.

No! She was not supposed to say that. So, the mermaid tried again.

"Cold?" the young woman asked.

The mermaid nodded her head quite excited. The young woman continued talking but she talked too fast for the mermaid to understand. Eventually the young woman understood that she needed to speak slower.

"You are not from around here", the young woman concluded.

"Nou", the mermaid confirmed smiling shyly.

"Are you lost?", the woman asked with a nice smile.

"Nou, I do not tink so", the mermaid answered in her odd accent and staccato voice.

The young woman asked several questions and for each answer from the mermaid she got more and more confused.

"It's clear that you have been in some accident and ended up here. I will get you a blanket to keep you warm and some soup", the woman concluded resolutely. She seemed to be a very warm hearted and determined woman and had fantastic thick, long and curly hair. The woman also had the most beautiful blue eyes she had ever seen.

The mermaid stood still waiting there in the middle of the empty restaurant. It sorts of resembled the inside of some of the shipwrecks at the bottom of the sea she had swam into as a child. From a swinging door the young woman appeared after a while, smiling at her with a blanket and a tray with soup and tea. They sat down and the young woman was quiet while the mermaid enjoyed the delicious soup with a glaring appetite. Understandably, she also enjoyed the warmth and the chance to rest her new legs.

This was the beginning of a long and great friendship between the Mermaid and the young woman called Charlotte. After they had been best friends for some time the mermaid, piece by piece, started to reveal her true identity. To protect the mermaid and to make it easier to explain the peculiar circumstances, they made up a story that the mermaid had been in an accident at sea and had been suffering from amnesia ever since. The mermaid moved in with the young woman who lived in a small house in the village. One day the mermaid began helping out in the restaurant which belonged to Charlotte's family. The family never learned the true identity of Lorelei. Then one evening Lorelei met Colbert, Charlottes brother. He and his magnificent blue eyes came into the restaurant with some friends. They all worked as fishermen. Colbert and Lorelei fell in love instantly. They started dating. But Lorelei pleaded to Charlotte to be quiet about her background to her brother. Colbert was totally crazy about Lorelei. He loved taking her to the beach and watch her swim. He had never seen anything like it. Sometimes he could stand there on the beach or on the cliffs watching her swimming and singing to the fish for hours. The only thing he found a bit odd was the fact that she was a vegetarian. She even refused eating fish or any other type of sea food. But she introduced some new dishes at the restaurant that became especially popular with the tourists travelling to the village from the big cities and with the younger generation. There were some totally vegetarian alternatives now. It was called vegan. Lorelei even got Colbert and some of his friends starting to "fish" for seaweed and algae instead of the normal catch. Lorelei and Colbert moved in together in the outskirt of the village in a house that had used to belong to Charlotte and Colbert's grandmother. After some time, they decided to get married. Colbert started his own company doing seaweed and algae farming and was from the beginning supplying the family restaurant with goods but soon started delivering to the whole of the coast. Lorelei that had helped out for some time as a seamstress at Charlotte and Colbert's mother's sewing studio in the village, now started her own studio and designed clothes that soon became very popular with the tourists. The magnificent designs and colours she created were something they had never seen before. Mesmerised embroidery in mainly lilac, green and turquoise colours filled her studio. Times were good and really happy. The wedding date was set. That year was the most fantastic summer in decades. Carefree they enjoyed each day and met up with the other young people from the village and hung out on the beach, at Colbert and Lorelei's house or at the family restaurant. The biggest problem was that Lorelei did not have time to help Charlotte as much as she should at the restaurant and that Charlotte did not respond the feelings and the courtship by the young man Vernon who was the little brother to Ernest, Colbert's best friend. Until one day. Colbert was helping his friends out. They were still working as fishermen. This day they all were down by the docks. Colbert, his best friend Ernest and Vernon. The two brothers had just been given an old fishing boat by their father who had invested in a new one for himself. Ernest and Vernon had already done some restauration work but now they needed help from Colbert to do the heavy repairing on land. When lifting up the boat there was a terrible accident. The boat came loose from the harness of the lifting crane and as a result the boat tipped over. Ernest was knocked down and broke a leg and hit his head on the ground and got a concussion. Vernon got seriously hit by the propeller and were bleeding from a severe cut in his upper leg. Colbert fell over and got the stern of the boat over him. Other people in the harbour witnessed shocked what was happening. A man came rushing into the restaurant where Lorelei happened to help Charlotte that day. Both women let go of anything they were doing and ran faster than a hurricane sweeping in over the bay. Soon after, Charlotte and Colbert's dad hasted down to the docks. Some people had called for the ambulance and others came to help out.

Lorelei had never practiced running so fast in her whole life. She outrun Charlotte, who was a good runner by all means. Not caring about her lungs nearly exploding and not feeling the acid in her legs, she was the first down by the docks. First, she saw Ernest. She put her hands on his head and chanted and then she put her hands on his broken leg, but Ernest whispered to her to save Vernon. Then she turned her head and saw Vernon next to the propeller with blood pouring out from his wounded thigh. Running towards him and fully focused on healing him she threw herself down on the ground and chanted and moved her hands over the thigh until it had stopped bleeding. By this time Charlotte had joined her. Like in a trance Lorelei recognised a pair of legs she loved more than anything else in the world. Her heart stopped and as she moved to the other side of the boat she also stopped breathing and felt the most excruciating pain and horror tearing her heart and whole body apart. She screamed – no one had ever heard a scream like that before. The scream was louder than thunder, more massive than the wildest hurricane and sharper than lightning. Charlotte witnessed Lorelei screaming and lifting the boat up and put it down a few meters away – away from the injured young men. Then she fell down on the ground and chanted cryingly while holding Colbert's still body close, close to her. Tears were flooding down her cheeks and wet Colbert's brown hair and ran down into his face. Charlotte watched the scene speechless with Vernon's head in her lap. It was like she was watching a movie. Their father was soon there next to Colbert and Lorelei and shortly after, their mother. Vernon and Ernest's dad came towards them. He went directly to Ernest. The ambulance came and there were many people down by the harbour and the docks now. The young mermaid could not let go of the young man she was holding even how much the ambulance people tried to move her away. They checked his pulse and concluded that there was none.

Dark clouds filled the sky and there was no more sun. The ambulance people now attended to Vernon and Ernest. There was not really anything they could do for Colbert. Even though it was a stressful situation they could not help but being surprised that Ernest basically was not injured at all but would be needing to get his wounds cleaned and checked. Vernon had miraculously stopped bleeding, but he was weak, so he was going to have to be in hospital for a few days and get proper stitches on the wound. Unbelievable, giving the amount of blood around him. Once they had checked the two brothers and put them into the ambulances, they started preparing for moving Colbert and went after a stretcher from the third ambulance. It was difficult hearing through the loud chanting from Lorelei. They talked calmly with Lorelei and said they were going to take Colbert to the hospital.

She had to let him go. In the end they promised she could join him in the back of the ambulance. The other ambulances had already left with Vernon and Ernest. Charlotte was hugging her mum who had broken down and were in pieces. Charlotte and Colbert's father was quiet and looked like he was in shock. He just stood there staring at his son as the ambulance driver managed to move Lorelei to the side giving them room to put Colbert on the stretcher. The ambulance nurse started moving Colbert into the ambulance. Charlotte heard how Lorelei stopped chanting and said they needed to get him ready. She wondered why they did not do anything. The ambulance nurse tried to explain that it was not anything they could do. It was too late. Lorelei screamed at them. When the ambulance nurse tried to stop Lorelei, she dragged him to the body of Colbert and insisted that he should check the pulse. He did. With total astonishment he called for his partner to hurry up. There was a pulse. Colbert needed adrenaline and hastily get to the hospital.

Dramatically Lorelei had saved Colbert, but he was still in an awfully bad condition as he reached the hospital. The doctors could not say whether he would survive or not. Colbert was kept in a coma. The weather changed radically and there were black clouds and storms. Charlotte could not get through to her best friend Lorelei. The mermaid kept herself to herself and took long walks with sand swirling around her and with her long dark hair dancing in the wind. Often, she swam out into the open sea even though the sea was so wild it looked like thousands of wild horses were running around in it. Charlotte and her parents did not really know what to do. Despite that they were all very distressed and afraid that Colbert would never wake up, they made sure that Lorelei ate and gave her a lift and company to the hospital. The miracle that he was alive and Lorelei's part in it, was never mentioned. It was said that the immenseness of Lorelei's love had saved Colbert. Charlotte also sat in Vernon's room for long hours. His dad was mortified and killing himself with guilt about letting the boys play around with the old fishing boat on their own. But no one blamed him. The young men should have asked for help and not tried to do it all themselves. That was the common point of view in the village, no matter how tragic the consequences had been.

One day Charlotte was watching Lorelei from a distance. Suddenly she saw how she jumped into the water from the cliffs at the end of the beach and swam out, far out. She swam so far out that Charlotte could not see her any longer. Anxiously she sat there waiting for a while. Then she stood up and started walking down to the shore. Even though the sun had not been seen since the accident and there had

80

been plenty of rain, the water temperature was not too cold. So, she took off her shoes, socks and lifted her skirt so she could walk out into the water. With the waves against her legs she walked as far out as she could but still there was no sign of Lorelei anywhere. For quite some time she walked back and forth and as her legs got numb with the cool water, she slowly started fearing the worse. What if Lorelei was so heartbroken after Colbert's accident that she has decided to do something horrible? What if she never would come back from the sea? Once the thought had planted itself into Charlotte's brain she ran as fast as she could, leaving socks and shoes on the beach, to the harbour and out on the jetty to where Vernon and Ernests dad was fixing stuff on his new fishing boat. Charlotte explained the situation without breathing. A bit shocked the man did what he was told and him and Charlotte went out to the sea to find Lorelei. Charlotte did not say that one of the things she feared was that Lorelei had decided to return to her home in the middle sea.

After nearly an hour of driving around searching for Lorelei, Charlotte finally noticed some bubbles in the water and asked Vernon's dad to turn off the engine. So, he did. Then they saw something coming up from the deep in a fast speed. Faster than any human possibly could swim. Concerned over what was approaching the surface they stood back waiting. Then with a swoosh and a flush the long dark hair of the green-eyed mermaid was up above the surface and she spat out water and breathed in large amounts of oxygen filling her lungs. Charlotte and Vernon's dad were surprised to say the least and astonished they looked at each other and then at Lorelei.

"So, help me up and let's go as fast as possible to the hospital. I need to see Colbert", Lorelei exclaimed with her strange accent.

So, they did. Lorelei asked if she could be alone with Colbert for a while. They stood outside together listening to the chanting inside the room where Colbert lay. A bit uneasy as it felt like they were eves dropping, they decided to go and see Vernon instead. Vernon was awake and eager to be allowed to go home. He looked cheekily at Charlotte and said with a smile he had a lot of things to do and could not just lay there rotting in the hospital. They went and got the nurse who found the doctor and they concluded that Vernon had healed better than they ever could have hoped for. He was free to go. When he had taken his belongings and changed his clothes, they stood outside in the corridor to fix the papers for his discharge. Suddenly the door to Colbert's room opened. Out from the room came Lorelei... and Colbert. Everyone looked at the couple stunned. After some seconds, the nurse ran up to Colbert and said that he could not leave the bed. They should just have called for them when he woke up and not walked out from the room. Annoyed the nurse pushed the couple back into the room and told them to wait in there until her and the doctor would come and examine Colbert properly.

Lorelei stops talking and takes a drink.

"Sooo is this really a true story?" Christophe doubtfully asks.

Both Lorelei and Charlotte nods quietly.

"Well, I always wondered a bit how you became so close friends and where you actually were from", he then says hesitantly.

Amberly looks at Lorelei with tears in her eyes.

"Aunt Lorelei", she whispers.

Lorelei leans forward and they hug for quite some time and cry for a bit.

Then Lorelei clears her throat and says she wants to finish the story before it gets too late. But yes, the little princess she sacrificed herself for was Amberly.

Everyone, doctors and nurses included, all were amazed over Colbert's recovery. The day after he was discharged. All their lives continued as nothing had happened. Charlotte convinced Vernon and Ernest that what they thought happened during that horrible day down in the docks, only where a coincident and that they all were just lucky. But the rumour was already established. Lorelei had magical healing powers and she became a myth already as a young woman. Colbert and Lorelei never spoke about it either. The only time something was mentioned was when after many years of marriage, they still had not been able to get pregnant. Lorelei only responded to that with: "you win some and you lose some".

The only one who knew the whole story was Charlotte, Lorelei's best friend and now a days her sister-in-law. Lorelei had swum down to plead to Membea to save her lover and husband to be. She had said she would sacrifice herself in exchange for Colbert's life. Membea had given her one option, and one option only. She could not trade Lorelei's life for that of Colbert's, but she could take away the option for Lorelei to ever be able to bear a child. Lorelei agreed to the deal. And that is how she saved Colbert. But as a result, they could never have children of their own. Of course, they had been very happy about the other children in their family and cared for them deeply. But once Colbert died of natural causes two years back, he still did not fully know the truth. Now Lorelei was not complaining. Surely as an old mermaid with two legs instead of the tail she got more and more problems walking. Being an old lady and having had a good life she was not regretting anything. But she needed to tell them that nothing comes without sacrifices. Big sacrifices, for a mermaid who chooses to stay ashore instead of returning to the sea. Especially a princess whose father the king was roaring the seas in the search for his dear daughter. The whole village would all be in danger until Amberly would return to the sea and to the King. And Lorelei that had once made the sacrifices to leave the sea in order to save Amberly and sacrifice her ability to bear children for her lover, could do nothing else than to be clear that Amberly needed to return to her father and make sure the King new she was safe."

"Now I need to have a proper rest my dear Stella", mum said exhausted.

Dad agreed, however much I argued it was the weekend. Mum promised we would continue and finish the story tomorrow Sunday but now it was bedtime. Up in bed my brain was spinning. What a marvellous story. This time for sure mum had exceeded herself in story telling! The whole night I dreamt fantastic dreams about underwater castles and cities, magnificent whales and funny and kind dolphins. Honestly, I also had some bad dreams about evil sea witches and octopuses, that wanted to put me in a prison and ask for ransom from the King.

Counting apple trees

Morning came and I woke up much later than normal. Before getting out from my room I had a lot of ideas for my English homework and even started writing them down on my laptop. It was about time. The homework was due Monday morning. That was tomorrow already. Down in the kitchen dad had made pancakes for breakfast. Mum was still in bed resting, he said. We had a quiet breakfast out in the garden. Today Spring was back again. It was already quite warm. The sun was smiling. Tonight, we were going to visit grandma and grandpa and have dinner with them. Uncle William was going to the hospital with his wife tomorrow, so it was going to be a family dinner before they hopefully had their baby on Monday. I was finally going to have a cousin! After breakfast dad and I went out for a ride on the tandem bike. We were going around the houses here up on the cliff. Some of the houses had much larger orchards than us. Furthest away, there was the big orchard with its cider house. Me and dad biked up there and dad said I should count the apple trees and if I got it right, I would get a surprise. Many people worked here. Uncle William was one of them. He used to be a fisherman together with dad before dad became a doctor. Now he was running the company and owning it and the orchard together with his wife. Her family had owned the orchard and the cider house for centuries. On the way back we took the scenic route via the path that ran outside of all the houses and orchards around the cliff facing the sea. We stopped and dad stood still looking out at the sea saying how extremely lucky we were living in this fantastic place. Plenty fish in the sea and plenty of apple trees here on the cliff above the village centre. I asked dad if he ever had counted how many apple trees there were in the village. He laughed and said that he had not. But perhaps they should ask William tonight. He might know. And surely, they would have to ask him about the number of trees in the big orchard where he worked. Otherwise, there was no way knowing if I got it right. When we got back Mum was talking to the roses out in the garden. Happy, I ran out to her and gave her a warm hug. Then directly I started asking for when she would continue the story. Dad thought we should wait until after lunch. Mum smiled at me pleading for hearing the rest of the story and then she said it was a good time to continue now since she had had such a long sleep in in the morning. As per the normal routine we all sat down in the winter garden and I waited impatiently for mum to start. She just needed to wait for dad to get his sketching papers and pens out. Then mum picked up where we left it yesterday.

"Anyone could clearly see how much Amberly and Christophe were in love. It was also apparent that William was opposing this. More heavily to begin with. But he seemed to be coming around. Each day at sunset he helped Christophe to take Amberly down to the sea. They took the van and drove through the village to where Lorelei lived at the outskirts, and then they drove down the small sandy road to the beach. This part was very isolated and normally empty of people so there was little risk anyone would spot them. First day they all got surprised when suddenly Lorelei appeared. Even more stunned did they get when she took of her long, knitted wool coat and underneath she had a typical made by Lorelei colourful swimming suit. Together she swam with Amberly and the boys could hear the two women splashing, laughing and sometimes chanting in that peculiar language. Every now and then they disappeared from the surface and were gone for so long that both the boys began nervously walking back and forth on the beach. They wondered how their old aunt nearly looked the same age as the mermaid when swimming, given how she struggled walking. As they gave Lorelei a lift up the hill and dropped her off at home, Christophe was noticing how the willow trees reached out their branches to greet her as she stepped out of the car. For the first time Christophe understood why Lorelei had got the nick name the willow tree witch.

Amberly practised her swimming and exercised her fin for several hours per day and improved fast with the help of Lorelei. Her tail was practically back to normal now. Even though it was understood by everyone that the reason for the hard and dedicated work with Amberly's rehabilitation was so that Amberly could return to the sea, Amberly and Christophe seemed to have forgotten all about it. At daytime they sat and spoke verbally but also using body language when words were missing. They read books and listened to music. William started complaining to his mother that the situation with the two love birds was getting unbearable. Christophe would only have his heart broken. Charlotte agreed that the situation was not ideal. When Lorelei visited, they often closed the kitchen door and had a private one to one talk. The fishermen in the village were getting very impatient. Without being able to fish as per normal they would soon start running out of goods to sell and get a shortage of money. They were very frustrated, and they could not understand how the storms could be so random and go on for over two weeks. The sea had not really calmed down yet and the day before a boat went under. The crew were luckily saved, and no one was physically harmed. It was clear to everyone that this could not continue. Lorelei understood that there was something she needed to do. Otherwise, it would be an uproar with the fishermen, and she would not be able to keep the village and the people in the village safe. On her way back she paid a visit to Ernest. So far, he had not mentioned anything about the day they caught the mermaid.

Through the years he never even mentioned what happened down at the docks, the day of the accident when Lorelei saved the three of them. It was a warm day for being end of October. However, since the weather and the sea were so unpredictable these days, that could soon change. If Ernest was surprised to see her, he hid it well.

"Hi, Ernest. I need you to take me out to sea on your boat and wait for me there while I have something I need to do. Obviously, I do not want you to say anything to Vernon and Charlotte about this. They would just worry without any reason", she said with her a matter-of-fact voice and peculiar accent. Ernest just nodded and then he put on his clothes and they took Ernest's car down to the docks.

Lorelei instructed Ernest where to anchor the boat. They had travelled far out. Ernest kept his stone face. He did not show any emotions when Lorelei said she would be gone max two hours, threw off her knitted wool coat, took a giant breath and jumped in to the deep, deep sea. Calmly he set an alarm on his clock, took up a book and sat in the captain hut reading. Down in the sea Lorelei swam and swam. She knew exactly how far she could go on for with that single breath. Every now and then Ernest glanced at the sea to check if anything required his attention. Since nothing was noticed, he continued reading. He had always trusted Lorelei since the first time he met her. Surely, she was special and not like everyone else. But since the day Lorelei saved them all down in the harbour, he had always had the highest respect for her. His wife, Sara, never got along with her. He never understood why really, and she never explained. But their daughter Rachel used to be at her place a lot when she was young. Perhaps Sara got a bit jealous of the situation. He never understood but guessed that Sara might have been offended by that special bond between Lorelei and Rachel. It was Lorelei that inspired Rachel to be a teacher. Sara had not approved when she moved away from the village to study. As a matter of fact, he did not really care about the reason for Sara's aversion. But after Colbert had passed away, they had seen very little of each other him and Lorelei. Ernest felt a bit guilty about that since he knew how much she was mourning him. But he had partly taken for granted that Charlotte, her best friend and Colbert's sister, would make sure she was alright. She had always done so, and they had always been so close from the day she just turned up in the village. That was a bit odd, he had to give Sara that. The village hade bloomed after she arrived. With all the tourist coming to the village the fishing industry had not been as important any longer. Basically, it was him and his brother that were the most active professional fishermen now adays. Sometimes he got the feeling it was thanks to Lorelei supporting them that they always had been successful with their fishing. Christophe would most likely go back to his studies once he was over whatever reason made him come home during the summer. Just like Rachel had done before she returned to the village. He had no reason to complain. They were well off and Sara nowadays only worked half time in Charlotte's restaurant together with their son Benjamin. He had been gone for a while educating and training to be the excellent chef he was today.

He could hear the waves lapping against the boat. It was soothing. One minute before the alarm went off Lorelei suddenly appeared splitting the surface and gasping for air. Once back on the boat he could not help but thinking she looked decades younger.

"Great if you can give us a lift out to the same spot exactly one week from now", Lorelei said once she had dried and was back in her clothes.

Ernest nodded and they returned to the harbour. Back at home he decided it was better to say nothing about this to Sara.

The reason for Lorelei going out to the sea was to dive down and visit Membea. Despite all the years that had passed Membea looked the same as the last time they had seen each other. Quickly Lorelei explained her reason for being there. In short, Membea needed to call for some dolphins that could send an urgent note through the ocean express to her brother, King Aenon, that his daughter was safe with her, his sister Lorelei. Most importantly, she wanted the King to hastily come here to Membea's cave one week from now to meet with her and his daughter. Membea had been overwhelmed and quite stressed out. Through her magic Membea could help air breathing creatures to get oxygen for some hours down under the surface. This time, just like the last time, Lorelei got two hours. With her whole heart Membea promised to act urgently upon Lorelei's request and make sure that her place was fit for a visit from the King from the middle sea. However, she needed some help from Lorelei with how she would be able to greet Kin Aenon in her simple home. Lorelei promised Membea that she would be richly rewarded for her efforts and have royal protection for a long time to come.

It was a sunny day and the sea had been calm for a few days and the men had been able to go out with the big fishing vessel. The same vessel with which they accidently caught Amberly with. It had been five days since Lorelei had gone out to the sea with Ernest on the small fishing boat. The doors to the front door suddenly opened just as Charlotte was getting ready to leave for the restaurant. Vernon ran in holding something in his hand smiling from ear to ear.

"We found it! Look, we really found it!" he exclaimed enthusiastically looking happy as a child at Christmas eve.

Charlotte first looked confused then she noticed what Vernon was holding in his hand. It must be the piece of jewelry Lorelei had been talking about. Vernon's enthusiasm rubbed off on her. Until she noticed that the token was broken into two pieces. Oh no, that could not be good news! Hastily she phoned Sara and said something had come up and she would be a bit later to the restaurant. Then Charlotte and Vernon went out to the car and took the magic token, the two pieces, with them. One was still stuck to a string of some greenish material, looking both like seaweed and gold at the same time, giving the token that was stuck to it a magical shimmering. The other part of the broken token simply looked like stone. In the car Vernon admitted that it was actually Ernest who had found it, but it was him who realised that it had to be the piece of jewellery that Lorelei had been talking about. William was sitting in the car waiting and muttered that he could not wait until all this madness was over. Christophe was already down by the beach with Amberly. He had not been out fishing today either.

Down close by the shore at the other end of the village they saw the truck that Christophe had taken. They parked the car next to it and went as fast as they could down through the rocky part after the parking and then took the sandy path down to the beach. Christophe was standing there looking out at the sea where they could guess two people swimming and diving down into the deep water and then popping up with a laughter. Every now and then they all could see a green glittering tail splashing in the water. It was soon sun set. Charlotte grabbed Christophe and told him what Ernest and his dad had found and she showed him the pieces she brought with her. Straight away Christophe started jumping up and down waving his arm hoping that Lorelei or Amberly would see him. They did and directly headed back to the shore. Lorelei got up while Amberly still stayed down by the shore keeping her tail in the salty water.

"Lorelei, they found it. But it is unfortunately broken", Charlotte said worriedly.

Charlotte gave the two broken pieces to Lorelei. With a strange voice Lorelei instructed Christophe to take Amberly out from the sea and told them all to stand far behind her. Then she placed herself with a straight back, eyes closed and with her legs steady in the sand while she started chanting. First the voice was very mild. Her hands raised and she had a piece of the token in each hand. The chanting increased in volume and intensity. In the horizon the sun was close to settling. The sky was amazing, and the sea was totally calm. As Lorelei's arms were reaching up to the sky her chanting had reached incredible levels. The sea started to move. Lorelei's hands were nearly meeting slightly in front of her above her head with her eyes intensively staring out at sea. They all stood there totally quiet watching. Even though Christophe was carrying Amberly in his arms he did not find this heavy. Finally, the two pieces of the magical token met and perfectly fit with the last rays of the sun just reaching it. Suddenly there was a flash from the token which shone straight out into the sea. The power of it nearly flung Lorelei back but she managed to stand tall and even though the sound from the flash was deafening you could still hear Lorelei chanting. The waves slightly parted and seemed to make a gate leading all the way to settling sun. Suddenly, a flash came back from the sun through the partly parted sea and hit the token Lorelei still was holding above her head. This time she could not stand up but flung back and hit the ground many metres behind her. Charlotte and Vernon hasted to make sure she was fine. Initially she laid fully still. Then with a fantastic laughter she sat up and showed them the token. It was whole. Afterwards they all went up to Lorelei's house for tea and biscuits and only Amberly and Lorelei fully knew how important it had been to find and mend the token for Amberly's future.

Back at the house with tea for everyone and Amberly's tail in a bucket with water and the magical token around her neck (where it belonged), Lorelei explained what was going to happen now. In two days, she and

Amberly would swim into the sea and meet king Aenon, Amberly's father and Lorelei's brother. Ernest had promised to give them a ride out with one of the small boats. Christophe wondered shyly if the rest of them could come along. Charlotte and Lorelei exchanged looks. In all honesty, Lorelei explained, she had no idea how the king would be reacting. If he was angry it was a bad idea that they were joining. The King might still be terribly upset with Lorelei for disappearing and for what she had done to his daughter. Vernon said nothing but reached out and took Christophe's hand in his. Amberly looked both happy and sad at the same time. Lorelei stated the day and time where they needed to bring Amberly down at the harbour. It was crucial that they did not forget to cover up her tail since it would be in the middle of the day."

"Time for getting ready to go to your grandparents bella Stella", Dad interrupted and pointed at the watch.

I wanted to hear more but mum promised that we would continue once back from my grandparents. I loved my grandparents and I so much wanted to see them. Of course, I wanted to see Uncle William as well. He was funny. He used to do take me out on the boat or let me climb the apple trees. For obvious reasons he did not have that much time for that now adays. And soon he would have less time. But I would have a cousin instead!

The Visit

My grandparents were in a great mood. They lived in a fantastic green house down in the village close to the beach. The restaurant next to it had been in my grandmother's family for a long time. Today we were not eating there because it was open to the public and busy with guests. We were in my grandparents' house where my dad and Uncle William had grown up. As soon as we got there, I started noticing the resemblance with the house and the house in my mother's story. The only thing that clearly differed was the big dining room facing the beach and the ocean. This was the living room in mum's story, but the living room in my grandparents' house was adjacent to the dinner room and in a round shape and with a huge fireplace. As dinner progressed, I could not help but thinking how much mum had borrowed from reality. During dinner I also realised that all the names were names from my family. Dad's real name was not Chris as mum and Uncle William called him. It was Christophe. And mum's name was Amber – so close enough. Mum's aunt's name had actually been Lorelei. It was nearly two years now since she disappeared. They had all been to a great trip to an Island in the Mediterranean Sea and on the last day she never came back from a walk down at the beach. I remembered how odd it all had been. It was like no one got as upset and sad as they should. After they came back home to the village, there was a ceremony in the Church. It had not been a funeral since there officially Aunt Lorelei was not dead. The police on the Island never found her body. No one really talked about her after the ceremony. Her old house was still used though. During the tourist season mum used to have it open as a combination of a museum and a design store. I had always loved the house. I could not help but feeling a bit disappointed about how little imagination she had used when it came to the names in her story, but it was also encouraging – I could do the same with my essay. Then I only needed one more hour to finish it. The food was amazing as always. Obviously, there were plenty of sea food and fish. But grandmother always made sure there were vegetarian alternatives, mainly for mum. After the delicious dinner and the superb apple pie we said our goodbyes and wished William and his Wife all the best for the coming birth.

As soon as we got home Dad went into the kitchen to put on tea, mum went out to the winter garden to get comfy and I put on my pyjamas so I could enjoy the rest of the story.

"Amberly was sitting very quiet in the boat. Part of her were so excited about meeting her dear family again. But she was also nervous and a bit afraid of how angry her dad would be. Her heart longed for her mother and sister Azalea. Well in honestly, she very much looked forward meeting all her family. Then she looked at Christophe and he looked back, and her heart started aching and she felt she could not breath properly. They were four persons on the boat. The two mermaids, Christophe and Ernest who was driving the boat. William was helping out in the restaurant so Charlotte could have a day off. Both Charlotte and Vernon were waiting back at Lorelei's house. The sea was calm and quiet. Lorelei was gazing out over the sea and after a while she signalled to Ernest that this was the spot. It was clear how much Christophe was struggling with keeping the tears away. After they had made sure that no other ships were close by Christophe took Amberly in is arm and with some effort put her in the sea. Shortly afterwards Lorelei dived into the water and the two women waved and swam a bit further away before diving into the sea disappearing with no trace behind. Even though Lorelei swam like she got younger for every stroke she took, Amberly took her hand and swam with Lorelei who was pointing out the direction. Soon they were close to the cave and the big impressive dark door. Further away there were traces of dolphins and there were marks from a carriage on the sandy bottom leading away behind the cave. Lorelei nocked on the door in the way she had previously been instructed to do and quickly the door opened, and Lorelei went first inside to get the magic help that made it possible for her to breath under the surface. Membea steered her further into the saloon and then warmly greeted Amberly before she made sure the door was properly locked.

In the saloon the Royal family from the middle sea was waiting. King Aenon anxiously stood up in the saloon twisting his hands. The room that normally was spacious looked quite small with the impressive King taking up that much of its area. His crown nearly touched the ceiling. Amberly was hiding behind Membea next to the lilac draperies hanging in between the hallway and the saloon. Lorelei slowly walked in. In the sofa, the queen and Azalea was sitting staring at Lorelei who was fully focusing on her big brother, King Aenon. King Aenon saw her, and his eyes filled with tears. He nearly looked the same. A few more grey hairs but barely any wrinkles. His body was still very muscular and the posture as stately as ever. Hesitantly Lorelei walked up to him with tears filling her eyes. She stopped just half a meter from him, and they stood still looking intensively at each other for a while. Then the king with tears running down his cheeks grabbed her and held her tight while he whispered:

"Lorelei, my dear little sister Lorelei, I though I had lost you forever."

While King Aenon and Lorelei embraced each other Amberly had sneaked into the saloon up to the sofa where her mother and sister Azalea were sitting. Naturally, they cried and hugged each other and then they cried some more. Finally, King Aenon let go of Lorelei and approached Amberly and now it was their turn to cry together and hug each other. After the initial reunion and when the tears had dried Membea served some drinks and seaweed snacks. She made sure to show Aenon to take the seat in the newly acquired majestic chair. It had cost a fortune, but Lorelei had compensated for it and it made Membea feel more comfortable to have the royal family in her home.

"There are obviously so many questions and I do not know where to start" the King said with his dark voice.

"We have been so worried and angry about you Amberly running away. At the same time, we are so enormously relieved to see that you are well dear daughter. And we got the extremely surprising and glad news to hear that you were alive Lorelei", he continued.

"I fully understand that dear brother. As I can only stay under the surface for a limited time, let me begin and then Amberly can stay. I will give you the big picture of what has happened and how I have lived up till now and then I will return tomorrow for another session", Lorelei said with a calm voice.

Her brother, the king nodded. So, Lorelei told her brother and the others all that had happened after that horrible incident at the market and the following events at the hospital. Without any sentimental emotions she described how she gave away the magic token for saving Amberly's life and how she therefore did not see any other option than to travel as far away as possible, where she also got some information from Membea that could offer her alternatives for her future. Lorelei smiled when she told them about how she got her legs that carried her to Charlotte's restaurant and eventually to Colbert and how after she met Colbert, she never considered returning to the sea and the life as a mermaid. She stopped talking when she came to the point where she walked into her sister-in-law's house and saw Amberly injured in the living room. By then it was not much time left so she hugged and kissed them all and said she would return tomorrow so they could continue the discussion.

The atmosphere changed when Lorelei left them and Amberly felt embarrassed. But Azalea helped and they soon started talking freely and after a while Amberly felt she could explain her reactions and tell them about her adventures and how she ended up being caught in a net that led to her meeting her aunty. Of course, her father King Aenon, showed mixed emotions. He told her how embarrassed and

104

angry he had been after she ran away and how much work it had been to smooth over her actions with the kingdom far, far away. But as the days passed by without Amberly being found, they all started calming down and became honestly worried for her wellbeing. Even that obnoxious young prince she was supposed to marry. Amberly's mother quickly intervened and said that the wedding was off, so she did not have to worry. Both the prince's family and they, her family, were in full agreement.

"Surely, it must be destiny that you found Aunt Lorelei though! Azalea exclaimed. They could all agree on that. Membea proudly served food and enjoyed being the hostess to the Royal family from the middle sea. Amberly was incredibly happy to be with her mother, father and her closest sister again. It was a much more pleasant reunion then what she could have hoped for in her most vivid imagination. Eventually it was time for sleep and Azalea and Amberly got some alone time since they shared the same little room. Azalea told Amberly that their cousin Muirgen now was engaged to that obnoxious prince from the sea far, far away. They giggled and concluded that the prince had no idea what he had got himself into. It would be quite an awakening when they finally got married and he would learn that she was not as sweet and easy going once you got to know her for real. They talked about their oldest sister Pearl and her family and a bit more about Nerida, the youngest one. Amberly missed them both. Then Amberly talked about Christophe. She could not stop. Even when Azalea fell asleep, she continued talking about him.

Back up in the boat Lorelei was thinking how even Ernest noticed the disappointment in Christophe's face when he realised that Amberly was not joining them back to the jetty. They returned and when Christophe dropped off Lorelei at her house, she took his hand and said he should not worry but make sure to pick her up at 11 o'clock in the morning the day after and bring a lot of coffee and sandwiches. Five to eleven the following morning he was back, and they all went out to sea again. Lorelei dived in and disappeared. Christophe felt sick to his stomach. He felt like he would never get to see Amberly again. Ernest tapped him on his shoulder and said all happens' for a reason and if things are destined to happen then it will. That did not make him feel any better. Ernest was sitting in the anchored boat with his book while Christophe was moving around and biting his nails. Suddenly, the surface split and there was Lorelei, Amberly and a woman a bit looking like Amberly, but that Christophe had never seen before. Shortly after with a laughter Amberly introduced Christophe and Azalea to each other. Lorelei got up on the boat but left the two mermaids in the sea.

"Are you prepared to meet my brother, Amberly's father, King Aenon and Amberly's mother, Queen Adella? Lorelei wondered, still catching her breath. Christophe nodded eagerly. Amberly smiled. Lorelei looked at Ernest and was just about to speak when he said:

"Two hours then. I'll set the alarm." Lorelei smiled at him and he nodded back with a grin on his face. It was late in October and even though it was a nice day and warm for the season, the water temperature was just as cold as it should be now. Therefore, Lorelei told Christophe to prepare himself and take four long slow deep breaths before he dived in. He should stay vey close to Amberly and preferably take her hand so that the shock for the body would not stop him from swimming. Christophe did not have to be told twice. He prepared himself, dived in and took Amberly's hand directly and further down they swam. The water was absolutely freezing cold, he could not think. It felt like he got a gigantic brain freeze. Amberly surely did more of the swimming than he did. Christophe was happy to be dragged. It was surreal and overwhelming. Cold water against his face and a burning icy sensation when his body was cutting through the cold-water masses passing by fish and sea weeds in a pace more feeling like a fast-forwarding film than reality. Then finally, they were knocking on a door to a cave, got let in and then both him and Lorelei, like magic, could breathe.

"Welcome to my humble house Christophe. Please accept this cape to keep you warm", Membea greeted. Christophe happily accepted the lilac cape with intricate embroidery. Amberly, that still held his hand, dragged him into the saloon. Christophe's first thought was how lilac everything was. Then he saw the King and the Queen both looking very majestic in front of him. Never before had he felt so small, naked and shy in his whole life. Awkwardly he did an attempt to bow, he mumbled and behaved like a total idiot. His limbs felt all clumsy and his movements all unnatural. To his surprise it seemed like Amberly was as uncomfortable and embarrassed as him since she was just standing there next to him and staring down on the cave floor. Eventually, Azalea came to rescue. She helped him with proper introduction and then they all sat down, and Christophe became more relaxed. Then began the interrogation. The King asked many questions and the queen a few more while her gaze penetrated his brain, trying to dig out every little thought he had ever had. Amberly was uneasy, Lorelei smiled encouraging and Membea kept herself in the background watching the show with big fascination. After an hour they started a more normal conversation. They talked about the future.

"Christophe, me and my wife, Amberly's mother, have discussed the situation and I have also talked to my sister Lorelei as you know as your auntie. As princess Amberly's and your emotions for each other are truly clear, we have a proposal", king Aenon proclaimed with his rumbling voice.

Christophe nodded silently. The King explained that Amberly had an education to finish. That was a must for a royal princess. She had nearly two more years before she was finished. This was more or less the same amount of time that Christophe had left of his own education. Therefore, the proposal was that they both would finish their studies and then they would meet again. This time Christophe would have to travel to the middle sea and Lorelei would accompany him so that he would find his way. If they still had these strong feelings for each other then the next steps would be discussed. The King and the Queen would be happy to see him as a guest in their palace. Until then Christophe and Amberly would be able to correspond via the Ocean Express and Membea and Lorelei would be assisting. They would not meet during these nearly two years.

Christophe knew he was supposed to feel happy and grateful, but he felt like his heart was going to stop. How would he be able to survive without Amberly for two years? Wise enough, he hid his emotions well and nodded his head and said what a fair and great proposition this was and how it was for the best for both him and Amberly. Before Christophe and Lorelei returned to the surface it was agreed that Christophe would bring his parents out on the boat the following day and then King Aenon, Queen Adella, princess Azalea and princess Amberly of the middle sea would surface to greet them before returning back home. Amberly and Christophe managed to steal a kiss before they parted. Lorelei had followed him home and had a long discussion with his parents. He did not participate but lay on his bed staring at the ceiling.

"You are really in love with her, aren't ya?" William concluded standing in the doorway. Christophe said yes and that he had no clue how to live without her. But as William said, he had managed before and he would manage now as well. Christophe knew he was right, but it felt so unfair. He did not want to manage living without Amberly. The whole night Christophe was tossing and turning.

They all woke up early. Even William wanted to join. Charlotte was nervous but Vernon showed nothing. He had a stone face. Yesterday evening Charlotte had asked Lorelei if Christophe could choose to be a merman. Lorelei had laughed and said that as far as she knew it was totally impossible – as a human you could only manage to stay down in the sea for a few hours, and that was with some magical aid. She had never heard of any magic that could transform a land man into a merman. That made Charlotte calmer. When the boat stopped and Lorelei signalled that all was clear, the surface soon split and there was

110

the Royal family from the middle sea: impressive, beautiful and surreal. They all greeted each other. King Aenon held Charlotte's hand for a long time and thanked her so much for taking care of Amberly but also for being such a fantastic friend to his little sister Lorelei all these years. Charlotte got embarrassed but also vey proud and happy. Vernon got told what a fine young man they had fostered in Christophe. William was speechless for the first time in his life. It was pleasant. Lorelei was all smiles. But for a split second she thought how fantastic it would have been if also Colbert had been there. Charlotte promised that the whole family would join Christophe for the trip to the middle sea to visit them. When it was time to say goodbye Christophe did not care about the cold but took of his clothes and came into the water so he could hug and kiss Amberly properly. It was a kiss that should last for nearly two years.

The Final Decision

They had all travelled back with the royal equipage across the sea. Part of the journey they had company from the group of dolphins she had met before. And the big blue whale also greeted them on their journey. Amberly was so extremely happy to see all of them and grateful for all the help they had offered her. Proudly she presented her friends to her family. Now they would help with carrying correspondence between Christophe and Amberly across the oceans. Two years went very fast. Before she knew it, the day before she was going to see Christophe again had come. Membea had been invited to support with her expertise and enable the humans attending the festivities in the palace. The night before Azalea and Amberly had been talking the whole night. It was so exciting but also scary. Today it would be an engagement ceremony between Amberly and Christophe with family only and Membea who would use her magic to give Amberly two legs instead of the tail. Amberly would still keep her token and she would still be able to breath under water. The transition would only be for a year and in a year, she needed to decide if she wanted to return to being a mermaid or if she wanted to stay on being a land person for the rest of her life. Amberly would live with Lorelei during the year of the engagement and then they would marry if Amberly choose to stay as a land person.

Membea also gave her the knowledge that as a land person her legs would work less and less the more years that passed. It was a fantastic sensation to use these two new legs and Amberly and Christophe made great use of them running around and playing tag on the beach. Then it was time to travel with a plane crossing the sea. Of course, it was the first air travel for Amberly. It had required a bit of Membea's special powers to organise a valid passport for the land person Amberly now had become. Flying was not something Amberly would ever learn to like.

The year as an engaged couple was an unbelievably happy year and during summer Azalea came to visit and stayed at Membea so that she and Amberly could see each other every day. Then came September. Christophe had opened a practise in the nearest city, and they had put down a deposit for a beautiful house to where they would move into after the wedding. First there would be a wedding in the middle sea and then they would wed in the church in the village. Both the wedding in the royal palace and the wedding back in the village were amazing. Christophe and Amberly were extremely happy and enormously in love. They lived a good life and one day it became even better when their little star came into the world. Both Christophe and Amberly were thrilled and life was great. After a few years Amberly started feeling a bit poorly, dizzy, and her legs would just not carry her as they had used to. Christophe, as the doctor he was, made her see all types of specialists but it was not so much they could do. Lorelei came over one day and they all sat down for tea and biscuits.

"Amberly, do you know why your legs are not really working any longer?" she asked kindly.

Amberly nodded but said she did not. Then Lorelei reminded her what Membea had said. The legs would not work perfectly. She would start getting problems as the years went pass. Amberly said she knew that, but she did not think it was going to be as fast. Lorelei reminded Amberly that she did not really sacrifice anything to become a land person, and she got a beautiful daughter. It was decided she would visit Membea. She did visit her that week already. As a result, Amberly lost her ability to heal and to breath under water. Before returning to land Membea gave her a very special seaweed in a jar that she should take when she felt the tingling sensation in her legs, lost strength or even if she felt any pains. And then Membea said that another consequence of the seaweed could be that Amberly would not be able to have any more children. Since that day the little family lived happily and their amazing daughter little star never got any brothers or sisters. Sometimes, Amberly struggled a bit with her legs. Every now and then they took the boat out to the sea to spend some time with Amberly's

114

family that came visiting. Some years they made a trip far away to the middle sea where they had a wonderful holiday and dived down into the deep sea and visited their family in the royal castle. One day, Christophe and Amberly decided, they would tell their daughter Star the story of how her mother met her father and how she got her legs. That day was soon to come."

Realisation

I did not know what to say. It was all a bit surreal and chocking. I guessed I should have seen it coming but I had just today at the dinner with my grandparents, realised the resemblance between the story and my life. I said goodnight to my parents and went up to my room. They stayed out in the winter garden. The sky was fully dark without any stars or a moon to brighten it up. Even though it was late I had to write my essay. I started with an idea yesterday and ever since the dinner at my grandparents the thought grew stronger and stronger. During the last part of mum's story, I had already the big picture ready in my head. It took a bit longer to write my essay than what I had thought. Way past my bedtime, I fell asleep content with having finished my homework. I knew I needed to have a couple of days to process mum's story before I would ask any questions. But surely there would be plenty of questions later on. Obviously, there was something my parents was keen on telling me but instead of saying it straight out they let mum tell this elaborate story. It was a very good story though, and it was great material and inspiration to my homework and my essay. The words just kept on flowing. It was and old school essay written on linear paper with a pencil. And I was quite proud of it.

The essay

With a steady hand I put my essay in the box where it was supposed to be handed in. Then I went to my desk. However, I did not sit down. Someone had put a big pile of glue on my chair. Not very subtle and you needed to be basically blind to miss it. But the three horrible trolls were not very bright. I changed my chair for the one belonging to the smallest of the trolls, the girl who had stolen my clothes. Then I sat down. A little bit later, so did she. After class it became a bit chaotic. The little troll overreacted when she understood she was stuck and could not get away from the chair. There was a lot of screaming and shouting. I just left the classroom to go and find Isac and Amanda during the break. I told my two friends what I had done. They both looked a bit concerned. The three trolls would for sure strike back. Who knew what nasty things they could do for revenge?

Later in the day in the school canteen they cornered me before I managed to reach to the table where Amanda and Isac where sitting. "You should be very afraid", the meanest one hissed with a threatening tone.

"I have no idea why", I answered with partly acted calm and

confidence. I was a bit intimidated actually.

"I know it was you and we will make you pay. I had to go home and change clothes and now my favourite jeans are ruined!" the smallest troll yelled standing so close to my face that if she had been a bit taller, I would have got some saliva stank in my face.

Then I said something stupid. I said that perhaps a good fairy had changed the chairs, but it was surely not me. That provoked the trolls, but I manged to find an opening and took my chance and fled to Isac and Amanda. Surprisingly enough, nothing much more happened that day. Calmly we walked home from school. The evening was quiet. We had a nice dinner and then I spent most of the evening in my room looking out the window. However, I did have a gnawing anxiety in my stomach when I went to bed.

The next morning Dad dropped me off at school. As soon as I had closed the door and waved goodbye and watched him drive off, I knew this was not going to be a quiet day. With uneasy steps and a foreboding feeling I entered the school building. Directly I saw that something was up. Many kids seemed to be busy reading something. Others were smiling at me in mocking way. Kids I had never spoken to. I was a bit late, so I went straight to my classroom. Today there would be reading aloud of the essays. Nervous as I was, I just took my seat and stared out of the window. Perhaps I should have been more attentive of the mood in the classroom, but my mind was somewhere else. Our teacher started talking about how many good essays the class had written and how difficult it had been for her to pick only three. Then she sat down and started reading the first which was a nice story about one of the boys and how he used to go on fishing trips with his grandfather. The second story was one of the twins telling a story about being a twin. It was quite funny actually. Then it was time for the third. The teacher only got as far as reading the title: "The Girl whose Mum used to be a Mermaid", then everybody turned to me laughing and started throwing badly made paper tails. I just sat there in my chair waiting for the teacher to interrupt, but she only did a lame attempt and let the commotion just go on until everybody got bored. With shaky hands she resumed telling the story about my mum who had problems walking because she was secretly a mermaid that had left her royal family far away to live with my dad as a normal human. Well, that was the short of it, but I am not even sure anyone heard the whole story. They were just making fun of me and calling me names. After class I grabbed my things and walked out into the corridor. There were, what I understood to be parodies of mermaid tails made of paper and plastics and all sorts of material, hanging everywhere and some sort of poster resembling a badly drawn mermaid baby with the letters: STELLA, above it. Very funny. Thanks for the anonymity! Suddenly I got a push in back. Then another one. I fell over. Landed on my stomach I felt that someone was pulling down my trousers and I started to kick and scream and try to turn around. It was the three girls. One of them grabbed my arms so hard that I could not move. The most horrible pulled down my trousers and shouted:

"Look, she does have a scar from a tail after all, the little mermaid girl. Come everyone and have a look!"

Kids started gathering around me and I just kept on screaming while I could hear many children laughing and making fun of me. It felt like it would never stop. But it did. Isac's big brother came to my rescue and chased the three trolls and all the other children away. Soon after, Isac and Amanda came out from their classroom with their teacher Rachel. Rachel asked Isac and Amanda if they could help with removing all the photocopies of my essay scattered all over the floor and remove the posters from the walls. Then Rachel put a hand on my shoulder and took me in to the Teachers room.

The real story

Outside the window in the teachers' room, I could see squirrels running up and down the big oak on the playground. It looked fun and boring at the same time. Things had not really worked out the way I had planned it. At first, I did not notice them entering the room, busy as I was feeling sorry for myself. Then mum's crutch must have touched something. Amazing how quiet they had walked in. Slowly I turned my face towards the sound and there was dad and mum. Behind them was Rachel. No one spoke for quite some time. Then mum came up to me and gave me a hug and dad came after hugging both of us. There was a nice silence in the teachers' room, and I started to cry. Mum cried a bit too. Both mum and dad whispered how much they loved me. I replied I loved them back. Softly Rachels voice and hand on my shoulder interrupted us. Mum and dad took a seat in the brown and beige striped sofa and Rachel sat down in the armchair next to me. It was clear how uncomfortable my parents were. Then with a soft and gentle voice Rachel told me that she had informed my parents of the events and also about some prior incidents. She had realised that I had not told them anything and therefore Rachel said, it was important that we had a proper talk at home.

At the kitchen table dad started talking. A year back mom had got the diagnosis multiple sclerosis, also called MS. He explained that mom was taking medicine that was aiming for slowing down the progression of the disease so that mom could live as much as possible without too many symptoms. Some symptoms came and went and right now mom was in a period of illness but that she might soon be better and be able to run and be quite normal again. Some people have more symptoms than what mom had right now. I looked at mum. She sat quietly and looked at me. I am happy that they finally told me the truth. We continued talking about how the disease was an autoimmune condition that would never go away, but with the great treatment there was today, it would help with keeping the relapses fewer and shorter. One day though it might be that mum had to sit in a wheelchair and then we would learn how to live with that. Dad let out a giant exhale. It was like he had held his breath for months. Perhaps he had. Silence came as a relief.

"Do you have any questions bella Stella?", mum wondered finally looking at me with empathetic eyes.

I answered that I do not. Then I wondered why they did not tell me from the beginning.

"How are you feeling now?" I asked.

"Quite good actually. I have a problem with controlling the muscles in my legs, but I will start doing aqua aerobics and then hopefully I am through this phase soon", she said with a happy smile. We talked some more, and I learned that mum suffered a bit from fatigue but that was normal. So, all in all, mum had got this disease, but it is not acute. Dad excused himself to make a call. After a while grandmother popped in with some nice food from the restaurant. Dad said to grandmother that they had told me now.

"Finally!", she exclaimed. Then she excused herself. She had to go back to the restaurant to let Sara go home. Tomorrow grandmother would be off since they were going to visit Uncle William and see the new baby. On the way out I heard her saying to dad that Rachel might stop by in an hour or two.

Dinner was delicious. We started talking about school and how I felt about it all. Dad wanted me to tell him and mum about the bullying and how it had started. I told them that I did not remember how it started but it had just got worse and worse over the last weeks. Obviously, dad wanted to know why I had not said anything. I explained it was because I did not want to worry them. I had noticed that they were already having enough on their minds and mum was poorly.

"But Stella dear, it is not your job to worry about us! We are the adults. We are your parents. It is our job to worry about you and make sure that you feel that you can come to us with whatever problem you have. Do you understand?" dad emphasized. I nodded and then we got interrupted by the doorbell. It was dad's cousin Rachel, Isac and Amanda's teacher. She came in and sat at the table. She wanted to know how I was feeling. I said I was ok. Then she started talking about a teachers' conference they had had at school discussing the situation that had been for some time with me and the three trolls. She asked if it was ok for me to switch to her class. The reason I did not go there already was because they were family but with the current situation school, she and my parents though it might be better. Of course, I wanted to change class! First Rachel was a better teacher and then my two friends also went to Rachel's class. However, Rachel continued, one of the three girls that had been bullying me would also be switching. It was important that the little group got split up and that school would work close with them and their parents to change their behaviour. I said I was ok. That was actually true. I did not think it would be any problems with just one of them. And since I would have Isac and Amanda there I was sure it was not going to be a problem. We agreed that I would start already the day after. When Rachel had left, we watched a film and I cuddled up close to mum. Dad carried me up

124

to bed when I pretended to be fast asleep.

In the morning it felt so much better going to school. Dad gave me a lift and walked me all the way into the classroom. He said hi to Rachel and smiled at me and left. Rachel started with informing that she had made some changes since I and the troll girl, named Maria, would start in their class today. Maria got seated next to Isac. He was not too pleased, but I think it was worse for her. From that day things did change. No one was pestering me at school any longer. Me and Maria became quite good friends. When summer break came, we all spent a lot of time down by the beach and mum usually sat reading on the beach but every now and then she joined us bathing in the sea. She was a great swimmer my mum.

One day after dinner mum said that we would go on a trip in September. Dad had managed to find someone to cover for him at the practice. I said it sounded excellent. But I wondered if we would be flying and if mum would have the strength. She assured me that she surely would. Then she gave me a peculiar look which I could not interpret and said she would probably feel splendid after the trip. I looked quizzically back. With a nearly dream like voice she said it was long time overdue and that there were some people we would go and visit that longed to meet her. Then she started with dinner.

Printed in Great Britain
by Amazon

87872675R00075